PIKO

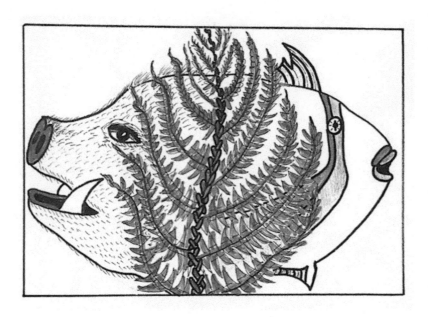

PIKO

A RETURN

TO THE

DREAMING

JENNIFER

LIGHTY

WHALE ROAD
KONA HAWAI'I

Cover illustration: "Feminine Wave" by Katsushika Hokusai
Frontispiece illustration: "Kino Lau of Kamapua'a" by Steven Lighty
Book design by Norman Minnick

ISBN: 979-8-9886370-0-4 (hardcover)
ISBN: 979-8-9886370-1-1 (paperback)
ISBN: 979-8-9886370-2-8 (e-book)

www.whaleroadpress.com

In memory of
Renate Schilling and Jada Delaney

"There was a time, in certain early cultures, where a sick person might be healed when told the mythological stories of the people."

—Rita Knife, *The Water of Life: A Jungian Journey through Hawaiian Myth*

nānā i ke kumu

look to the source

CONTENTS

PIKO

1. umbilical cord, navel

2. summit of a hill or mountain

3. crown of the head

4. crown-less woven hat

5. end of a rope

6. border of a land

7. tip of an ear

8. center, as of a fishpond wall or kōnane board

9. place where a stem is attached to the leaf, as of kalo

10. source of the world

INTRODUCTION

O NCE UPON A TIME people believed a culture was main-
tained and a life could be saved by stories and ceremony. Some still do. I am one of those people, a living tes-
tament to how story can heal a sick body and a damaged soul.

Once I would have begun this ceremony by reciting my lineage in order to place myself in time and space and invoke the
guidance of my ancestors going back to the stars, but I am the
descendant of Europeans who crossed the Atlantic, migrants
who left their villages for reasons not passed down, a daughter
of lost forests.

I don't know what motivated my ancestors to leave Europe
for an unknown land. Maybe some were just adventurous spirits, but more likely most left because they had to. Perhaps there
was a famine, or they were persecuted for their political and
religious beliefs. Maybe, like so many migrants, they wanted
more opportunities for their children. Whatever the case, they
claimed what didn't belong to them, nearly erasing the stories
and cultures of the land they occupied. Turtle Island, where the
Woman Who Fell from the Sky found refuge, became North
America, named for the Florentine explorer Amerigo Vespucci.

I feel the loss of what my ancestors took without permission, and I feel the loss of what they left behind—the fern-spun song of the spring where they gathered water, the stream just outside the village lined with curly dock and cow parsnips where spiderwebs sparkled at dawn, the rivers they followed to the ports where they boarded ships with all their worldly goods to be carried over the edge of a map to the place marked "Here be dragons."

I invoke my ancestors now through a bloodstream, rich and pulsing. I honor the severed umbilical cord of my lineage by providing it now with fertile ground so my ancestors' lineage can complete its potential through me. I am the ground. I am their legacy, and if I am the result of a forgotten lineage, it's up to me to remember where we came from. As I remember, I banish this amnesia, with your permission—for us all.

On April 1st, 2021, I sat at the edge of two small anchialine ponds in the Pu'uhonua o Hōnaunau, the Place of Refuge, on Moku o Keawe, known in modern times as the Big Island, and told stories to the water from many cultures: Hawaiian, Haitian, Irish, Inuit, Greek, Sumerian, and Shinto. Day after day, I wove myself into the place with words. I opened my senses. I watched. I listened. I smelled, touched, and tasted. I felt… and I wrote.

As the ceremony evolved I found myself weaving my own lived experience of trauma into the narrative along with observations on the climate crisis, ecocide, and the legacy of colonialism in Hawai'i. This book is the resolution of my own trauma through reconnection with nature and the words here are the result of the sacred exchange that occurred between me and the elements. My wish is for this book to activate your own internal compass. Everyone's path will be different as we collectively navigate the massive transformations occurring now on Earth. We all have important parts to play, but the directives must come from within. We can no longer rely on outside forces to tell us what to do.

This book is grounded in Heka, Mū Hawaiian magic. Those of us conditioned by Western culture to view magic as something fanciful, may not realize it's actually a system with principles and rules that, much like a scientific formula, enable us to produce concrete, measurable results. According to Heka, a spell consists of three parts: invocation, banishment and administration. This formula is a law of nature, a cosmological constant, that governs creation on Earth. Heka is both science and ceremony, a means of creation through holistic consciousness using both brain hemispheres. What could our planet become if we bridged the gap between logic and imagination and channeled the unified power of our brains? Born in a left-brain, masculine dominant culture that worships logic and relegates imagination to fantasy, I'm not advocating for a return to the feminine right-brain. I'm proposing an advance to the holistic, that we cultivate an androgynous vision and expand our concept of creation beyond our current limited materialistic view to include ceremonies and spells. As each one of us aligns our consciousness with the highest good of all life on Earth and beyond, we shall invoke the qualities necessary to move into homeostasis, banishing whatever we discover that keeps them from manifesting on Earth. Sometimes those qualities may sweep broadly across our whole culture, but more often they will be aspects of ourselves that need to shift and evolve. Every human on Earth is essential to the whole. Individual actions matter.

I may not know the stories or the ways of my ancestors when they were still immersed in an indigenous consciousness—knowing themselves and their place in the cosmos through relationships to plants, rivers, streams, deer, bear, and boar, but I am here now. I am proof of my lineage, and while I may long for what was lost, I will no longer define my life by it. I will use the body my ancestors gave me to learn the stories directly from nature. I claim connection with the stars and proclaim my lineage through the living entity of a language sourced from within my bones and blood, held within the greater matrices of forest, ocean, lava field, and waterfall.

Words are spells. My hope is that this book will help humans reconnect to our primal origins and realign with our divine potential through surrendering to the greater powers of nature. All around us, even in cities, pigweed pokes up through sidewalk cracks, pigeons offer weather reports from Peregrine falcons soaring high above skyscrapers, stones carrying the deep dreaming of Earth's molten core envelop passengers on the subway, and underground rivers are still in touch with the clouds, and wherever water came from in the first place. Everything we need to save the world is right here. We just need to believe in ourselves.

Where do stories come from? Many aboriginal and indigenous people today say they are the voice of Earth herself, and believe that telling stories is an essential role in keeping the balance between human culture, our home planet, and the cosmos. A well-known example of this today would be the Shipibo people of the Amazon, who say their icaros are direct transmissions from the plant medicine ayahuasca. Although many modern cultures have lost their stories, if it's true they come from beyond human sources, they could still exist and are waiting to be resurrected and broadcast through a human voice box. In the meantime, thousands are still with us, passed on through the oral tradition and preserved in books. We need these stories.

I have witnessed in hundreds of people, the craving for deeper connection, and held space for the individual griefs of this collective loss through years of teaching, traveling, and working with clients as a bodyworker on the table and in the water. One thing I've learned from all my experiences, is the mind will only get us so far. *Piko: A Return to the Dreaming*, moves beyond the intellect and its explanations and rationalizations. Reading it requires some work. This is not a linear narrative moving like a line down the highway at top speed, it's a meandering dirt road. At times, it may not even be a road. I write this way in order to invoke embodied participation on your part. Because it is a spell, be forewarned that it will require vigilance. If you choose to allow the words to penetrate you, you may be moved to your own invocations. Remember, any invocation must be balanced equally by a sacrifice. I can tell you I had to sacrifice my own sense of inadequacy over and over again during the ceremony and in the process of writing this book. Every time doubts come up again, I administer to them by asking why they are here and if there are any actions they want me to take in the world. In this way, I show my commitment to my kiakahi, my purpose.

It's important to me to give proper credit and outright gratitude to Martin Shaw, whose book, *Wolferland,* was the inspiration for my ceremony and book. Reading the story of Martin's 101-day vigil on Dartmoor in Devon, England, is my idea of a thriller. Martin is a pioneer who uses images to invoke his readers to explore new territory. Without *Wolferland* and Martin's body of work, written and oral, mine might not exist. I hope this book honors what he has so generously passed down.

Anyone who has been blessed to listen to Martin tell a story, will know the experience is both bespoke and collective. For over ten years I experienced this by the shore of Lake Damariscotta at the Great Mother Conference in Maine. Not only did his words shine light on my wounds and triumphs, they did the same for everyone else in the hall. Every year, as the week unfurled, the events of the stories he told permeated our everyday interactions. The "conference" was really an alchemical crucible of the highest order and I am forever changed by it.

Ironically, it's hard not to reduce the impact of our shared experiences at the Great Mother Conference with words, especially a linear account of what happens during the week. The best way to describe it is mycelial. As the story evolves you individually, it's also evolving the other hundred or so folks sitting in the hall. When the fungal threads reconvene, as they inevitably do, the convergence evolves the stories, too, keeping them alive in the fertile ground of human bodies who have perhaps learned a little about how to navigate like a blind mole under layers of living soil. In this way, it's the linear narrative that is proven to be the fantasy.

In *Piko*, I hope to incite this same process in the reader by bypassing the flat highway and driving us on a curving mountain road of narrative streams and literary techniques. Here you will find a tapestry of memory, poetry, folk tales, reflections, and song lyrics that I hope will keep the reader from the comfortable dissociation of a good read. Although I love a good page-turner, I don't think we need any more books to lull us to sleep. I suspect waking up will, in the long run, be much more satisfying, even if we don't get the happy Hollywood ending we crave or think we deserve.

At the Great Mother Conference we speak of the "handmade life," a life lived on purpose according to one's destiny. I'm hoping that by disrupting the linear narrative readers will awaken to the power of stories to cast spells by becoming aware of the field of transformation that activates when we engage with language in a sacred way. My hope is, as a species, we'll remember our purpose on Earth and commit to fulfilling that, instead of destroying ourselves and losing this opportunity to participate in the evolution of the cosmos through our greatest gift, love.

Finally, despite the illusion of density and permanence we've created by following a path away from nature, even today, with the night sky smeared by artificial illumination and smog, there *are* some cultures where people can recite their lineage back to the stars. The names of their ancestors are incantations containing cellular memories that bind the speaker to the truth of where we came from and where we are going as the human experiment unfolds. I am fortunate to have encountered one of those people and to be in close relationship with him as my mentor.

Ke'oni Hanalei is a descendant of the Mū Hawaiians, a mysterious people often associated with legends of Lemuria, who lived in the Hawaiian Islands before the Tahitians sailed across the Pacific around 500CE to settle the islands and establish what we know as Hawaiian culture. Most of what I've learned from Ke'oni has been transmitted orally, so at times in this book, you'll hear me say, "Ke'oni says..." without citing a further reference. You'll find directions to his work in the notes at the back of the book. I would, however, like to clarify that the Mū doctrines and the wisdom of the ferns contained in pua'aehu-ehu, fern medicine, operate differently than what those of us educated in conventional Western school systems are used to. They are not something to be memorized and applied, they are an activation. Much of what I learned from the ferns can thus be seen as remembering, and this book is my direct testimony about what they continue to teach me.

Lemuria was an ancient civilization. The Mū however, are still here. According to oral records, Mū, which predates Sumeria and Egypt, is one of the seed civilizations on Earth. Traces of it are still found in symbols around the globe. Basically, if you're alive now you are Mū.

Through the medium of pua'aehuehu, Ke'oni shares Mū teachings on emotional intelligence that have been preserved in the DNA of ferns. Millenia ago, when it became clear human culture was about to be destroyed by catastrophic earth changes resulting from the abuse of technology, 103 known ferns volunteered to encode the Mū teachings in their spores. The ferns were the perfect vessel because they had reached evolutionary stasis, meaning they couldn't be genetically altered, ensuring the wisdom of Mū would live on uncorrupted. Ke'oni has named these teachings "the principles of aloha." Each one is an initiation all humans must navigate and integrate in order to fulfill their role in the human experiment, which is to embody aloha mā, self-reflective love. This does not mean to love yourself in the way we're exhorted to do by New Age culture, although I'm not knocking that. Most Westernized humans are so immersed in shame we could benefit from more self-compassion, especially if it leads to atonement and corrective actions to heal the distortions of colonialism and war our culture has enacted on our planet. Rather, aloha mā is a direct experience of totality, a shamanic knowing that you are an aspect of God, or however you want to define the holy force of creation. It is the ouroboros, the snake consuming its own tail. Once you experience it, you are consumed.

Buddhists would say it's stepping off the Wheel of Karma and tell stories of Bodhisattvas who, having done this, choose to come back to Earth to assist humans. According to the Mū, once a person has integrated all the principles of aloha mā, they hala, or ascend, meaning they don't come back in physical form. Instead, the integration of all the principles results in the collapse of amnesia and the remembrance of one's divinity, making a contribution to the human experiment by upping the odds we'll be successful at seeding the next world with love.

Many indigenous cultures today speak of different epochs of life on Earth as "worlds." The Hopi say we are currently in the fourth world. In the first three, most of humanity was destroyed because of war and other destructive practices. Hindus say each universe passes through four yugas before being destroyed and reborn. The Kali Yuga, happening now, is the fourth. According to the Mū, the experiment of the last age was electricity, and this experiment was successfully seeded in our age by the he'e, the octopus. Will we channel the electrical forces gifted to us by the last world and become a conduit to pass aloha mā on to the next?

Without my own ceremonial lineage to reference, I relied on intuition and things I'd been told or read about to create this ceremony. I am not Hawaiian and was aware the whole time I was in a very sacred place that had been colonized by white settlers, my human lineage. I earnestly do not want to be part of the wave of colonization my ancestors rode, turning Turtle Island into North America and Hawai'i into a tourist destination to be consumed for entertainment, but I'm also aware of the waves beyond the waves that carried my ancestors over the Atlantic. Where did they begin?

Humans have been displacing other humans as far back in history as we know. Is our species inherently greedy? I don't believe so. Instead, I will explore in the book how our impulse to conquer and colonize is a result of primal wounds to both our feminine ('unihipili) and masculine ('uhane) energy centers that have resulted in distortions that keep us disconnected from our aumakua, the androgynous center that contains both principles and gives us access to the non-binary consciousness we need to see beyond the polarizing beliefs that keep us in conflict on an inner level, with our fellow humans, and Earth herself. As Ke'oni teaches, the 'unihipili establishes safety. Those who don't feel safe approach the world from a stance of defense, and since the task of the 'uhane is to be the hero of our lives, to take action, the distorted masculine goes on the attack in a misguided attempt to fulfill its kiakahi (purpose). This theme will become more clear as I share how this unfolded in my personal story in relationship with a local Hawaiian when I first came to Moku o Keawe 27 years ago, although back then I called it the Big Island like every other colonizer.

I'm sure I made mistakes. I may have offended the spirits and the local Hawaiians. If so, I am sorry. If someone who reads this feels I need to make a correction, please let me know.

One of my great poetry teachers, Fran Quinn, insists that mistakes are how we learn the most, and I've heard that even today in indigenous cultures, children are not as carefully guarded as they are in modern industrial society. If they put their hand in the fire they get burned. Hopefully next time they won't do it so they can grow up to have two hands to make all the things only humans can—embroidered shirts, feather cloaks, engraved silver nose rings, finger paintings, and murals of feasting gods on the ceilings of domed temples.

And of course, there's Rumi and Leonard Cohen reminding us that cracks and wounds are where the light comes through. It's embarrassing to be a clumsy, ignorant human without a lineage who has to make up her own ceremonies, but I did it anyway because I want to become a worthy ancestor, reweaving my broken lineage for us all through a relationship with the particular ground I stand upon. The stories we need are beneath our feet. They always have been.

ZERO POINT
A PROLOGUE

Kealakekua Bay, Moku o Keawe

Barefoot in bathing suits,
Marina and I scan for fins—
the dolphin pod coming in
to calm water
after hunting all night
in the starlit ocean.

Hikiau heiau at our backs—
stacked black stones
worn by wind and salt.
Signs say kapu—keep away.

We are haole, foreigners,
but this was always

a sacred place, forbidden
to commoners like us.

Here, the priests once spoke to gods
with blood sacrifice:
Ku, Kāne, Lono, Kanaloa.
The stones are hungry—
you can feel it.

Across the bay
we see the monument
mounted above the reef
where tour boats pull up
to drop off snorkelers,
site of Captain Cook's murder.

Cook's men attempted
to kidnap a chief,
Kalani ʻōpuʻu, aliʻi nui,
hostage him
for a stolen longboat,
but the people surged to shore,
surrounded the sailors.

Nuaʻa struck
and Cook went down,
stabbed in the heart
with a knife he had traded
to men who had never seen metal.

First white man to sail into this bay,
but not the last—
his death still reverberates
through the sacred water.

Kapuhakapu,"Forbidden Flower,"
the water is named.
So beautiful, to pluck it
was an affront to the gods,
the bay off limits to all but ali'i.
(And here we are about to jump in
like we have every right to.)

We are ready
to leap off the rocks,
but the water remains unbroken,
an illusion of stability
like skin. Salt

corrodes the bulkhead
and cakes our pores,
merges with inner waters.

We are more fluid than the clay
we were told we are made of.
White spray unfurls in air like ferns.

Mesmerized by the amorphous aqua,
incantation of breaking and reforming,
endless suss and sigh of sea—
Marina sees it first,
summons my gaze to the surf line
with a slow-motion shriek.

Like a bullet
commanding the waves to open
it hurtles toward us on the bulkhead,
flip-turns at our feet,
white belly a lightning bolt

that rattles the ground beneath us,
a radio dropped in a bathtub—
shark!

Electrified and numb
I see its teeth and forget the sight
immediately. "Whoa!"
we proclaim in unison.

Marina says, "That's at least eight feet."
I say with little wit, "More, I think."

What would have happened
if Marina hadn't been
slow to get going this morning?
That big joint
she lit in the truck
on the way down the mountain
slowed us down
even though I didn't smoke it.

We decide not to enter
but are back the next day,
crossing the live wire
left by the shark's passing.

We swim into the azure
where the pod welcomes us
like family. We, too,
must breathe on the surface.

We float,
look up at the pali
where chiefs' bones

were honored in caves.

Kealakekua, Pathway to the Gods:
Ku, Kāne, Lono, Kanaloa—
I dare to chant your names
knowing sharks sense blood
from miles away.

Today we are bathing
in clicks and whistles
and the pod
drums our cells with sonar,
seeing right through us.

Yesterday's fears
not even a memory—
we swim in that same water,
closer than ever to freedom.

The story begins
with a shark at our feet.

CHAPTER 1
WHAT'S THE NATURE OF MY GAME?

◎

I RIDE IN ON "Sympathy for the Devil," a tinny blast of bravado from my phone on the empty passenger seat. *Please allow
me to introduce myself. I'm a man of wealth and taste.*

Well, not really. I may have taste, but wealth? And I am a
woman, a woe-man, woefully so sometimes, in a body stalked,
then judged when it doesn't conform to what the devil wants
from me. But let's skip the politics and woe is me and just say
my chariot is a silver Honda Fit with bashed-in hatchback, duct-
taped bumper, and a stink from wet dive gear that won't dissipate. It's April 1st—Fool's Day. The Stones got it right.

> I've been around
> for a long, long years
> Stole million man's
> soul an faith

My goal: Pu'uhonuanua o Hōnaunau National Historical Park,

the Place of Refuge, an ancient sanctuary where, in the wā kahiko (pre-colonial era also referring to mythic time), people who violated kapu could be absolved of their transgressions and escape execution. Kapu was sacred law, and according to my standards seems arbitrary and dictatorial, but in this time and place I'm what some call a white settler colonizer, also known as a haole, a foreigner who doesn't have the right to judge or the ability to understand the deeper meaning behind the restrictions. Judgment is a dead end anyway. I want to move forward into unknown territory.

I'm approaching by land. Once, Hawaiians had to *swim* here—across Honaunau Bay, known to many as Two-Step, a famous snorkel spot where tourists frolic with the tropical fish and test their fears of the abyss by swimming past the reef into bottomless water, where one breath can be the dividing line between life and death, rapture and a blackout there's no coming back from.

Anyone can die here, even the locals. There's a monument to one who disappeared a couple of years ago on the bottom close to shore. You can swim out and see it, but remember one thing:

His body was never found.

Never turn your back on the sea, I was told 27 years ago when my feet first touched this island, unable to feel that the black lava rippling out from my soles was actually alive. I had no premonition that simply setting foot on this island created from fire rising up from the bottom of the sea would alter the course of my life in ways I never could have imagined growing up in Connecticut.

Just as every cop is a criminal
And all the sinners saints

As heads is tails
Just call me Lucifer
'Cause I'm in need of some restraint.

Surely, I'm not in need of restraint? I'm one of the good haoles, aware of colonialism and the negative impact of tourism on the local people.

Tell me baby, what's my name?
Tell me honey, can ya guess my name?
Tell me baby, what's my name?
I tell you one time, you're to blame.

Am I the devil? The same as every other clueless tourist or wealthy tech bro buying up Hawai'i and forcing the locals to move to Las Vegas so they can afford to buy a house and have a decent job, or gamble, drink, and drug away their pain? I don't have money to buy any land. In fact, I can't even pay rent. Right now I'm a member of the class known as work traders. We pull weeds, paint shacks, harvest fruit, and clean Airbnbs. We are people without money who are willing to work for no money in order to get to live in Hawai'i. We don't have much influence or power, but if we all decided not to work we would. I wonder what the Hawaiian economy would look like if property and business owners paid their help? That's a serious question, not a sarcastic one. Should we all walk out? Being liminal people, interested in the knowledge that can only be gleaned and the transformations that can only occur on the edges, I doubt, as a mass, we will. Ultimately, I'm not really the one who gets to say I'm the devil. That right belongs to whoever perceives me as such. That also doesn't mean I have to accept the label.

I do want to say I'm not the devil, but if there's one thing I've learned in my 27 year relationship with Hawai'i, is that these dripping green mountains rising up from the sea for thousands of feet to puncture the clouds releasing the rain with endless names, these rumbling volcanoes, and fields of lava rock sharp as blades; these waterfalls shifting to rivers that flood so fast you can find yourself stranded for an entire week in a houseful of addicts pretending not to notice they will soon be out and end up scraping the residue that owns them off the floor; these waves with hidden currents that will suck you out to sea, your body never found by searchers; these islands, the most remote land masses in the world—they will test you. With "hard" lessons, especially when you are arrogant or innocent enough to say, even to yourself, something like "I'm not the devil." So maybe I am the devil.

> I shouted out
> Who killed the Kennedys?
> When after all
> It was you and me.

But I'm maka now—aware of it. Does that let me off the hook for past mistakes?

> Pleased to meet you
> Hope you guessed my name
> What's puzzling you
> Is the nature of my game.

In the tarot, the Fool steps off a cliff with all his possessions wrapped in a handkerchief tied to a stick. A little white dog yaps at his feet. Is the dog warning him or urging him on? We don't know. It's up to interpretation. The Fool doesn't stop to answer our questions, he just goes for it, steps off the cliff, because boots are made for walking, which is what I'm doing now as I slide my Honda Fit under a tree outside the park gate and slip around the guardhouse making my way toward the park pavilion. The Stones echoing in my ears, I walk toward the building erected on top of the lava that rumbles when Mauna Loa quakes. I pass behind the tourists listening to the guided tour of a mural depicting the ancient Hawaiian ways.

Why don't you take out those earbuds and look around you? I want to say, but I keep on. Head down, I imagine myself slipping into a fox skin and slipping between the tourists' and rangers' legs without being seen. I don an invisible cloak. Even if they can see me I must imagine they don't. I am in search of the mythic, not the modern.

Yet the modern is here. Many of the locals I see on a daily basis are descendants of Hawaiians who survived against the odds when white settlers brought syphilis, smallpox, tuberculosis, influenza, gonorrhea, measles, mumps, cholera, leprosy, and now COVID-19 to these islands. By 1840, 84% of Hawaiians were dead. In 1898, the Kingdom of Hawai'i was annexed by the U.S. government and has been illegally occupied ever since.

Past the pavilion, I reach the Great Wall, 600 years old, 12 feet tall, 18 feet wide, 950 feet long. I may be a stupid colonizing haole with no right to be here, *and* I want to converse with this place, discover it directly, body to body, skin to stone as the daughter of the Earth I am.

On my home island, Block Island, originally named Manisses, I left pinches of tobacco for the spirits when I roamed the deer meadows and snapping turtle swamps. In Mexico, I left corn. I heard locals here offer Pele gin so I bought a bottle of Tanqueray at Target. I'm worried the park rangers might nab me for carrying booze in an open container, so I poured a few shots in a travel mug I clutch to my chest as I make my way through the park. It seems ridiculous to be worrying about rangers when making an offering to a goddess that is a volcano, but that's the world we live in. The sacred is now something you get ticketed for.

I know that gin is a product of British colonial oppressors, so I don't feel so great about it as an offering, but I figure it's better to show up with something than nothing at all.

"So what?" I didn't swim to the Place of Refuge. I'm still here. My feet have carried me to the Great Wall. Black stones stacked high above my head, each one heavier than my body. They jut into the air as if they could pull the sky down and swallow it into Earth's molten core. Here, it's impossible to forget about gravity. I stand before the gap that marks a tunnel through to the ocean constantly shifting from one shade of blue to another, the ultimate shapeshifter. Time to walk through.

A black-crowned night heron, auku'u in Hawaiian, steps out of the grass at the edge of the royal fish pond in the wall's shadow. He watches me as I pour gin onto the gravel.

> Auku'u,
> here in the west
> you stride
> out of the long grass
> when the sun
> sizzles on the horizon.
>
> All day you wait
> at water's edge.
> No one sees you until
> that one step:
> the grass crackles.
> Your beak
> is a lightning bolt
> charging the water.
>
> You gulp electricity,
> alive and whole,
> swallow
> and are still standing.

The fish down your gullet
die slow in the sudden dark
still swimming.

When you see me
you freeze. The one eye
turned my way,
blood-red and beady.

Soon
the sun will be gone, swallowed
by the other side of the world—
the one we can't see—
also spinning.

Teach me how to stalk
my shadows, how to
dream my way through the dark
and follow signs
beyond human words.

I take the first step. Walls, 18 feet wide, swallow sound like a
dragon waiting on the other side of a black hole for whatever
makes it through. I trudge over roiling lava sprouting succulents that remind me of home marsh—Andy's Way at low tide
where glasswort gleams at low tide after hours underwater.
I'm in Mordor with Gollum on my tail. It's easy to imagine him
climbing up from a crevice to drag me down by the ankle gasping, *Pretty! Pretty!* It would also be easy to trip, and the lava, as I
mentioned, is sharp. I am careful and make my way to another
stone structure closer to the ocean.

   This will be my spot. Stone walls open to the sky, nothing
inside them. Originally these walls probably had a thatch roof.

Now they are open to the sky and seemingly without purpose, like a wall built to mark a territory no one wants to claim, but I was told a king once sat here on a stone facing Honaunau Bay to watch the swimmers trying to make it to the sanctuary.

On April 1, in the year 2021, in the 21st century, I proclaim for the next 21 days I will keep vigil where the king once sat watching the waves roll into Honaunau Bay.

A human fetus starts exchanging oxygen and carbon dioxide through the placenta at 21 weeks.

At its best, the human brain can maintain attention for 21 minutes.

The human body loses 21 grams of weight after death.

(Some say that's how much the soul weighs.)

There are 21 cards in the Major Arcana of the tarot.

(There are really 22, but the Fool is represented by zero, which doesn't actually exist.)

The 21st card, the World, bears the image of a hermaphrodite and represents totality.

21 is the legal drinking age in the United States.

You can vote or get drafted at 18, but 21 is the age my culture deems a person ready to handle spirits.

It's so easy to get lost in reverie, to lose the power of the moment. I proclaim I will pay attention because I know distractions are the real devil.

Back to here—this rock. I'm embarrassed I don't know the name of the King. Should I look it up? Pre-colonized Hawaiians could recite their genealogy for hundreds of generations, maintaining a link that went back to the first humans born of clay and water, activated by breath and fire. Some still can. I know the names going back to my great-great grandparents on both sides, but before that is mostly blank space. This ceremony is for all the ancestors who've been forgotten, as well as the humans who will come. Tonight when I get home I will look up the King's name.

I turn and face the wall, not touching the stones because someone told me I could absorb "bad" energy. When I asked what that was I was told, "energy that wasn't necessarily good for me." In any case, not touching the stone wall feels respectful.

How were the Hawaiians able to hoist these stones without a backhoe? The rock faces are smooth as if sanded, and without gaps like trees grown together, adapted to each other's angles and curves.

Should I sit on the King's Rock? There's no sign saying I shouldn't. I wish I was more confident, but I've seen so many other new age haoles like me claim authority from guides I never hear. Either they are way more tuned in than I am, I don't have any guides, or they are making it up so they can claim an unearned authority that makes me cringe. *Please don't let me be like them,* I say to myself silently. Right now, all I hear is my own guilt about being a haole echo in my head.

I pour out some gin as a preemptive apology if I'm violating a kapu. I'm sure back in the day I would not be allowed to sit here, but the King has been dead a long time and it's really time for these hierarchies to transform.

The stone is warm, still holding the sun like a lion's belly.

When I sit I feel the contentment of knowing the lioness is out on the savannah hunting wildebeest. I will feed soon. It starts to rain, small pricks that burn my skin as the sun goes down.

Tide pools in front of me, beyond the wide bay, and beyond the bay open ocean that goes on forever, the blue horizon that calls for me in the black night.

How far am I willing to go for this ceremony? Am I willing to suffer? Am I willing to be uncomfortable? Am I willing to receive grace?

I don't have clear answers. All I can do is begin. So, feeling like a fool, like a stupid haole, I speak anyway. I don't want to be a ghost anymore. I chant the Mū prayer received from Ke'oni on Instagram.

> Kā' eka to'e a mea
> ite ohn parat'u
> lā mea a mā a mā
> kuhi ewa a mā
> a te a mā

I take a deep breath when I finish the first cycle and begin again. Finish, then breathe, repeat a third time, and then begin again in English, my brain's language, hoping to unite my body and mind's memories.

> To be entangled in that which is unnatural
> Now I rise, exposed and brilliant, finally!
> And to penetrate an illusion
> Finally, finally!

Here in the Place of Refuge on Moku o Keawe I make my first ho'okukāla, my proclamation:

Creator,
Help me see through control's haze
to clear water.

Grant me the slipperiness of the eel
and the lark's bright song,
going down I will need it.

Guide me to the spring's source
where the water is in love with the clouds.
Release me
as cooling rain on the mountain.

Help me let go with a deer's grace
when a new form calls me;
shape-shift from mist to waterfall,
forest pool to rock-tumbled rapids.

Strike me like an iron bell
resonant with ocean thunder.

I will know the ecstasy of being eaten,
be someone else's food.

I bow to the whirlpool.

CHAPTER 2
LOVE BITES

I HAVE SPOKEN holy words. Made my proclamation. Now it's time for a story.

A few feet away ki'i of Lono, Kāne, and Ku look out over the water. (You may know them in a debased form as tikis in Polynesian-themed restaurants where their grimacing faces often adorn scorpion bowls nobody should really drink.)

The bones of kings are still worshiped right here. Recently, I watched a young man who was a descendant of Kamehameha the Great, rinse gourds in the ocean, preparing them for ceremony. The Hawaiians say the mana, the spiritual force of a person, is in the bones. That is why they were worshiped, and still are, despite the screeching tourists tripping everywhere through the park on the razor-flamed lava. A king was not a figurehead, or a symbol, or a tourist attraction like we see today in Great Britain, the country that first colonized this island. A king's mana was so powerful he could sustain his people. Like the Grail King of Arthurian lore, his health kept the people in right relationship with the kingdom. Even dead, his bones could speak. People listened to those stories and fed the bones with praise.

That young man I saw washing the gourds—he probably knew stories the 'aina told his ancestors when humans first fell from the sky into this world. When I met him I was too shy to introduce myself. *I don't deserve to be here,* was the usual refrain running through my mind.

Maybe I shouldn't be on this sacred ground, but the fact is that I exist and I'm here. I am not a movie. I am not a projection. Underneath my skin, bones make blood that will flow if punctured and feed the black lava with my essence. I am here. I will offer what I can, even if it's inadequate. I will no longer be a stranger.

The fact is, according to the calendar, I do have some history here. 27 years ago, when I was 26 years old, a friend of a friend picked me up at the Kona airport and drove me south and up a steep hill to the sketchy hospitality of a coffee shack. I say sketchy because there were a lot of men living in rickety structures all over the mountain. (One of them showed up in my room in the middle of the night right before an earthquake.)

But before that, on my first evening in Captain Cook, one of the less sketchy invited me on a motorcycle ride. I clung on like a terrified possum down the steep winding road to the water. When we stopped I slid forward in what seemed like slow motion, burning my right calf on the tailpipe. Even though the burn was so bad my skin instantly blistered, I said nothing. I pretended nothing had happened as the guy enjoyed showing me the view I couldn't really see. My physical eyes worked just fine, but I was so uneasy in my skin that I constantly slipped out of it to float above my body. It's hard to see anything with any depth when you're so busy dematerializing.

We were right here. The Place of Refuge. I still have the scar on my right calf, on the meat of my right gastrocnemius. I had no idea then, what a choice cut I was, and that sharks were circling.

NANAUE THE SHARK MAN

In the time of the reign of Umi, a great chief of Waipi'o Valley, lived a beautiful girl, Kalei. Her hair was a thick, black wave to her waist, the wind's playmate, and tiny i'iwi birds stole strands to weave into their nests high up in sandalwood trees, leaving her feathers she collected to weave into capes and headdresses for the ali'i. Her hands were deft and her feet, never bound by shoes, were so broad she never lost her balance walking through the valley's streams.

Kalei was very fond of shellfish and often went to a bathing pool near the ocean to pick 'opihi. Even the crabs who sunned on the rocks admired her, staying above the waterline when she climbed over the sea-slick lava rock to pry off the briny bites, mouthfuls of ocean in the shape of a cone-shaped hat.

Usually, some of the other village girls went too, but one stormy day they all passed when she asked if they wanted to go to the bathing pool, so she set off alone delighting in the rain, for she knew if it fell hard enough waterfalls would burst over the rim like old friends returned from a journey, full of tales from the clouds. She was looking forward to a swim. The pool was safe and sheltered from the gigantic waves that rolled in from the open sea, and she wasn't afraid, just thrilled by the storm's wildness.

Now I have to tell you, this pool was also a favorite spot of the shark god Kamohoali'i, and one of the reasons he loved going there was because he had seen Kalei dive from the rocks so gracefully she slipped into the water without a splash—not a ripple. He hid at the bottom looking up at her, afraid to show himself because he didn't want to frighten her, utterly enchanted by her beauty. He longed to make her his wife. Kamohoali'i knew he could grab her in his jaws and take her, but he was far more chivalrous. He had made a pact with the first humans not to hunt them and meant to honor that.

You may be surprised to learn that about sharks, but they don't want to kill us. If they do bite, it's by mistake, and if you've seen one swimming in the big blue as I have, you'll know they stalk their prey with the exquisite precision of a Toledo steel sword etched with flowers and vines that only grow in the deepest gulches, the places known only to humans brave enough to climb up vertical faces, risking death by landslide. You'll know they move through the water like mercury, fluid and contained, and Flamenco guitar shoots out of their whole bodies when they explode in a streak of lightning, electrifying the reef. Even though you can't hear the music, it shakes the water like a subwoofer, touching the primal.

So yes, Kamohoali'i had big, sharp teeth, two rows of them, and rippling muscles that could take a lover to the edge of death until they begged for release, but he wanted more than that with Kalei. These days we call it consent. If he took her, he would kill her. If he let her escape she would forever fear him. So with the elegance inherited from 450 million years of ancestors, he resolved like a Medieval troubadour to court her, transforming himself into a very handsome young man who glowed like the rising sun as he walked toward her over the rocks where she was picking 'opihi and eating the shellfish right there, mouthfuls of ocean that filled her with a strange longing.

Sleek and agile as an eel, Kalei usually had no problem sticking to the rocks with her tough, broad feet, but that day a wave surged higher than usual, sweeping her off her perch into the sea. "Auee!" she yelled, but there was no one close enough to hear. She would have been swept out to sea if a young man, broad of shoulder, with gleaming white teeth, hadn't risen up through the waves to save her. Kalei was so grateful and charmed by his strong hands and solicitous black eyes—he looked at her as if she was good enough to eat, his work was easy. She was ripe for the picking, as they say. She had no idea the dashing young man had summoned the great wave that had almost taken her himself, and if we're being honest here, she probably wouldn't have cared. Kamohoali'i was a smooth talker, a deft lover, and had a heart with infinite depths that could love even her darkest parts. She felt safe.

They lived together in ecstasy, cradled by the green gulches of Waipi'o, although Kalei did wonder why her husband would only come home at night.

"Kalei, why your man no show his face in da day?" the villagers asked, looking askance at her swaying hips, flushed cheeks and dilated pupils. "What he hiding?" But she felt no need to explain anything to them or ask her husband why she couldn't see him in daylight. Eventually, she became pregnant and Kamohoali'i, a just and ethical man, revealed his true nature. You can imagine her shock when she found out her lover man was the shark god, and then her grief when he told her he would have to leave her. She would have to bring up their child alone. You can imagine how it would feel to discover the father of her unborn child was the most feared creature of her people. Still, she loved him and was stricken he had to leave.

Kamohoali'i left her very specific instructions on how to raise their child. "My love," he told her. "You must *never* feed our child meat. He will be born with the instincts of a shark and the ability to shape-shift into other forms. If he gets a taste of meat the results could be deadly."

Kalei swore she'd never let a morsel of meat touch the lips of their precious child. They kissed goodbye through passionate tears, teeth clashing. Kamohali'i wanted to devour her, but he leaped into the sea, shifting back into his shark form. Kalei watched his fin sink beneath the waves, tasting his kiss long after he was gone. Her lips were bleeding.

In time she gave birth to a beautiful, healthy boy she named Nanaue, who was normal in all ways but for one—on his back, between his shoulder blades, was a shark's mouth complete with two rows of razor-sharp teeth that snapped at her when she tentatively reached out a finger to see if they were real. Kalei loved her son despite his " deformity." Whenever she looked at him she saw his father and remembered how it had felt to lay with him in the dark and feel his teeth nuzzling her throat, the sharp points moving up her jugular vein before swallowing her lips with a kiss as deep as an ocean trench never touched by sunlight. "Oh my love, how I miss you," she would sigh in the night. She had confessed her husband's true nature to her family and they agreed to help her hide the hideous jaws on her son's back. They were afraid if the village found out they would deem him a monster and death would be his fate.

She knew her son was not a monster. She wove a little cape of kapa, tree bark cloth, and made him wear it all the time, which for a little boy was quite a trial. Not only was it hot and uncomfortable, the other boys teased him. "Eh, Nanaue, why you wearing one cape?" they jeered.

Nanaue, like most kids, just wanted to be normal and grew to resent his mother, who began to lose sway over him as he grew. But there were many years of joy between the two of them before that resentment blossomed. One of the things they loved to do together was hike to a waterfall pool deep in the valley. Here Nanaue got to take off his kapa cape and swim freely, chasing the little fish and splashing without fear anyone would see the jaws on his back.

And then, one day, right in front of his mother's eyes, he changed into a shark as soon as he hit the water and promptly ate every fish he chased. Not one escaped. Dread sank like a stone sinker into Kalei's belly. She knew this was just the beginning.

In that time there were many kapus, sacred laws, the people had to follow. The kapus were enforced by the ali'i—chiefs and priests. Death was the punishment. One of those rules was that men and women could not eat together. When a boy became a young man he stopped eating with his mother and auntys and took his meals in the mua, the men's house. Because he had no father, Nanaue's grandfather was the man in his life. And Nanaue was such a fine, handsome young man, tall and straight as a sandalwood tree. His grandfather was rightfully proud of him and hoped he would grow up to be a famous warrior. When it was time for Nanaue to leave her house to eat with the men, Kalei at first begged her father to let him stay with her. When she saw that was not going to happen, she begged him to remember Kamohali'i's instructions. "Please, father. I swore to his father I'd never feed him meat."

"Kalei, we breaking kapu if I no take Nanaue to da mua. You wanna see your son put to death? Boys need meat. If we feed him only poi and bananas he'll change into one woman."

And so Kalei's father ignored her entreaties, stuffing Nanaue with pork and dog meat that caused him to grow even bigger and stronger. He was the most impressive boy in the village. All of his friends were envious. He had no doubt his grandson would be one of the most ferocious and brave warriors of Hamakua.

"Da boy fine," he told his anxious daughter. "Human blood stronger than shark." Nanaue's grandfather watched over him like an i'o, the hawk who drafted down the mountain to pluck bright-feathered i'iwi from the sky, but eventually, the old man died and Nanaue lost his protector. He was now dependent for food on his uncles, who all roasted him about his voracious appetite, even tossing him their scraps and bloody bones to see him scramble on the floor. "Kalei's boy one glutton," they sneered. "Like one dog. Let's make him do tricks."

Nanaue didn't hear them. His senses were totally locked in on the scent of blood on bone scraps, the alluring aroma of rotting marrow. They had no idea how soon they would rue their mean-spirited mockery.

Nanaue was a lonely boy. He didn't understand why he had

been born this way. He hated the jaws, the ghastly teeth he could hear clacking on his back all night. How could they be a part of him? He hated his cape and the way his mother was always following after him telling him he had to keep his back hidden. He never felt safe or free to be himself. Eventually, he gave up trying to play with the village boys who taunted him about the cape and spent most of his time hanging out by himself at the two pools, the one in the sea where his mother and father had met, and the one at the base of the waterfall in the back of the valley. Everybody gossiped about him because it was not normal to wander off by one's self in that time. Everyone talked about his cape and wondered what was beneath it. He felt like a freak. Even though he was a beautiful young man, he hated himself, and because he held himself apart, the villagers began to call him stuck up, not understanding he had to stay away from fear he would kill them. Sometimes he could hear their blood thumping under their skin and had to run away.

Nanaue did have one good quality according to the villagers. He was devoted to his mother. He was often found helping her in the lo'i, the kalo patch. People on the way to the ocean would see them working together knee-deep in the muddy water, or on their way to the back of the valley to swim at the waterfall. One year, around the time Nanaue began to eat meat, the villagers were surprised to find him suddenly social. "Brah, where you going?" he would ask as they passed by.

If they answered "da ocean," he would say, "Brah, be careful. You no like disappear." *What he mean by dat?* the villagers thought. *So strange, Kalei's boy.*

Around the same time, something even stranger began to happen. People were starting to get bit by sharks on a regular basis, which hadn't happened for as long as the elders could remember.

And then it got worse. Solitary swimmers started to disappear.

The villagers searched the water but never found a trace of human remains. They still didn't suspect Nanaue, whose mother was so terrified she tried to keep him close at all times, but without his grandfather, he fell under the sway of his no-good uncles and stepfather, who told him not to listen to his mother. "You like be one man?" They teased him. "Grow a pair and no listen to your madda."

Kalei wept whenever someone passed them in the lo'i. Nanaue looked at her with contempt and walked away, following his friends and relatives to the ocean. It was too easy. He entered the water as a man and swam right up to them, shifting in a thunderclap to a shark. One bite was all it took. There was nothing in the world as satisfying as holding a terrified, thumping-hearted human in his jaws—fear was delicious. The harder they thrashed, the better the taste. It became harder and harder for him to return to a human body. All because his grandfather hadn't listened and fed him pork and dog meat.

Over and over again it happened. The villagers were terrified and King Umi had no idea what to do, although being King he didn't admit this. Kings must not show fear. Instead, he organized a work party to bring the village together and build morale. They would clear a large area to raise sweet potatoes and kalo. Everyone was required to go, and they all did, except for Nanaue who stayed behind to help his mother tend her garden and lo'i. The men were astonished—no one disobeyed the king—and turned him in.

Nanaue was ordered to appear before King Umi. "Why have you disobeyed my orders?" demanded the King. Most other young men would have been afraid, but not Nanaue. He answered with the cockiness born of having a pair of man-eating jaws on his back, "Because I had other things to do."

"Other things!" Umi was outraged, but he also admired the boy's boldness and splendid physique and decided not to punish him. "Boy, you will make a great warrior, but you need discipline. Show up tomorrow for help with da work and we can forget this. I remember your grandfather. He was a good man. Those uncles and that stepfather aren't raising you right. From now on, look to me."

These words would have made the heart of any other young man swell with pride, but Nanaue knew that not even King Umi was a match for him. He showed up for work the next day only to please his mother, who he still loved, even through the blood call of the beast. Of course, he had to wear the kapa cape, which was dreadful and cumbersome in the hot weather. The other young men teased him, finally growing bold enough to snatch it off his shoulders.

"Monster!" they bellowed when they saw the snapping jaws. "Look at da blood on his teeth!"

Inflamed by their own blood lust, the young men would have killed him if they could, but Nanaue was much stronger, severing wrist veins and jugulars with his teeth as they tried to grasp him. Finally, enough men came to restrain him and they dragged him to the King by his feet.

"Nanaue da one killing our families!" the men exclaimed in a frantic muddle.

Umi looked at the snapping jaws on this handsome young man's back and the choice was clear. He proclaimed: "Put him to death." The fine young man was no warrior, but a monster. He turned his back on the boy as the villagers started gathering wood for a huge bonfire because the only way to kill a shark man was to burn him down to ashes.

As Nanaue watched the pyre being built the desire to live flared inside him. He called out to his father, "Kamohoali'i! Save me!" and the shark god endowed him with superhuman strength that enabled him to burst his ropes. He fled from the warriors to the ocean pool and leaped in, and in plain sight of his entire village, shape-shifted into a shark and he swam into the deep ocean out beyond the reef.

Irate, indignant, and terrified, they seized Kalei and Nanaue's uncles who had helped hide his secret, and brought them before King Umi. "Kill them!" they bellowed even louder in a feeding frenzy.

Umi, a wise king, considered the nature of Nanaue's father, the shark god. Umi knew that Kamohoali'i was not a vicious beast, that his killing had a purpose, and that he was generally beneficent, though of course unpredictable as wild creatures are. He saw that it was not a good idea to kill his relatives. Kamohoali'i had lived among them. He had married Kalei, a woman of their own village. He had known love as a man and a beast. Clearly, it was wrong to kill his wife, and he also reasoned that if he killed Nanaue's family there would be no one around to keep him in check if he roamed the coast hunting them, and he could even make his way upstream through the underground tunnel from the ocean to the waterfall pool where the people liked to bathe.

"No, let them live," he pronounced. "We may need them to calm this wild beast they've raised, and remember it's not the boy's fault. If his grandfather hadn't fed him flesh none of this would have happened. He could have lived more human than animal. Set them free. Priests, make an offering to the shark god so we can hear his desires in this matter."

Kamohoali'i heard their plea and took possession of one of the priests so he could speak again as a human. This is what he said: "I am grief-stricken that my son has violated our pact and killed your people. It was never my design for sharks to eat humans. It's his grandfather's fault as you know. If you need to blame someone, blame him, but I will take care of my son."

"Will you kill him yourself?" the villagers asked.

"I will not," Kamohoali'i replied. "I will banish him. He can never again swim along the shores of Hawai'i. If he does, my shark officers will execute him without a second thought."

The villagers were disappointed because they wanted the

blood debt to be paid, but there was nothing they could do in the face of the shark god's will.

"And one more thing," Kamohoali'i continued. "Kalei is my wife and I still love her. If anyone in this village, including King Umi, harms her or her family I will command my son to come back and terrorize you for the rest of your lives."

Fortunately, Nanaue had no desire to go back to Waipi'o. He had already forgotten his mother as soon as he'd crossed over the reef's edge into the black-tinged water. The villagers honored their agreement with Kamohoali'i and didn't harm Kalei, though they were never friendly. She lived a lonely life.

Banished from Waipi'o and Moku o Keawe, Nanaue swam to Maui and came ashore at Kipahulu, resuming his human shape. People asked him who he was and what he was doing there, suspicious of this handsome stranger who had turned up out of nowhere, but he was so beguiling they accepted his flimsy story of being a traveler, and one of the local chiefs even gave him his sister as wife. Nanaue didn't really want to marry her because he was afraid she would discover the jaws on his back, but he didn't want to draw attention to himself by refusing, so he married the chief's sister and made a pretend vow that he had to remain chaste, insisting they sleep in separate houses.

He did his best to deny his desire for human flesh, but eventually, the craving was too strong and he again started killing. Like before, it was too easy. All he had to do was walk up to these new friends as a human and push them into the sea, leaping in after them as a shark and ripping into their warm, juicy meat. Eventually, he was caught in the act by some fishermen on the rocks he hadn't noticed and fled across the ocean to Molokai where nobody knew him.

On Molokai, he lived at Poniuohua and it was not very long before he was at it again, pushing people into the water and devouring them. Hot-blooded. Check it and see. If only his grandfather had not fed him that pork and dog meat!

Nanaue actually thought this sometimes. He was still half-human, and longed to be a man as much as he longed to eat men. But he couldn't control himself. After a time, the terrified people of Poniuohua went to a shark priest for advice. It had reached the point where they were unable to fish because it was unsafe to go into even the shallowest water and they were starving. The shark priest looked within and told them to hide by the shore and wait for Nanaue, the stranger who had appeared out of the blue, so dashing and handsome, so helpful and friendly, always willing to lend a hand; he made butterflies flutter in all the girls' stomachs when he passed by. It couldn't be him, they thought, but the priest insisted. "He's not what he says he is."

The burliest men of the village obeyed the priest. They hid, and when Nanaue appeared on the ocean path, they leaped on him and tried to restrain him. Nanaue was so strong he shook them off, but not before they pulled off his kapa cape, and there it was, his dirty secret exposed once again for all to see, his shame. The frenzied jaws snapped on his back between his shoulder blades.

Terrified, Nanaue fled, running down the path to the ocean, but the men caught up with him and bound him so tight there was no chance of escape. Once again he had to watch as the villagers gathered firewood to build a pyre to incinerate him. Even if he had begged for a faster death by beheading (which he wouldn't have), the villagers would not have relented, for it was known that a shark-man can only be totally consumed by fire, otherwise, he could come back and take possession of a harmless shark who had never thought to hunt humans, turning that shark into a man-eater.

Nanaue was exhausted, not just from the struggle with the men, but from a whole life of hiding who he was, of struggling against his instinctual nature. In his mind, he was ready for the fire. He hoped his mother didn't mourn him forever, and that his father the shark god Kamohoali'i would honor him in the shark way, circling with his fin above the water at dusk until the sun sank and the darkness rose up from the depths and took over, offering humans the chance to overcome their terrors and fears.

But the instinct of his body to live was stronger than his mind. As he lay there watching the people build the fire that would take his life, the tide came in and he saw that if he rolled over his feet would touch the water. As soon as the first wave lapped him he turned back into a shark. Someone noticed and raised a cry and the people stopped stacking wood on the pyre and threw nets over him, entangling his fins in a tight web. This, along with the shallowness of the water, stopped him from using his monstrous strength to break free. As they beat him with clubs and pierced him with spears, he heaved toward the breakers, growing weaker from blood loss, and he would have got clear of them if they hadn't called on the demigod Unauna, who lived in the upper mountains of Kainalu. In truth, only another god could defeat him, and Nanaue was stronger than Unauna, but he was also bound and hampered by nets. Unauna defeated him and the villagers dragged Nanaue up the slopes of Kainalu to the waiting pyre.

You can still see the mark of his passing in the shallow ravine leading up to Shark Hill, and the stone around which Unauna tied the rope to haul the shark up. Nanaue was so immense that his wounded body oozed such a great quantity of blood and water it put the fire out several times. Unauna saw the danger in this and told the villagers to cut bamboo from the sacred grove of Kainalu to make knives to slice the shark's flesh into strips that dried out and burned completely. It took the whole grove, and Unauna's father, the god Mohoali'i, was so angered at the desecration of the sacred grove that he stripped the sharpness and edge out of the bamboo that grew there so that to this day it is different from the bamboo on all the islands. Unable to cut or pierce, useless for anything but shelter and shade, and the sound it makes as the wind passes through it from mountain to sea.

Nanaue, beaten and burned
for being himself
a killer.
The flesh tasted so good!
Remember how the men mocked him,
called him glutton?
They were the ones
who called up his bloodlust,
feeding him dog meat
when his mother
had begged them not to.

Kalei knew what would happen.
Her beautiful son,
glorious in his feather cloak,
bold and strong with shark blood,
was not born a monster—
he was made one.

Yet the fear in the villages
where Nanaue stalked!
The grief of the other mothers—
sons and daughters lost
to Nanaue's ravenous jaws,
the weeping widows
mourning unfulfilled lives.

Could Nanaue have stopped himself?
Kept the pact between humans and mano

proclaimed by his father Kamahoali'i?

Kalei, living alone
for the rest of her life.
Mohoali'i's grove desecrated.
Humans afraid of sharks,
forgetting kinship,
losing ancestors,
the web of life
broken.

This is what I hear after I tell the story, sitting on the King's seat watching the waves roll into Honaunau Bay—ee ee ee ee— the cry of an 'ulili bobbing through the sky on a high-pitched lob. Wandering tatler, winged nomad crossing the Pacific from Alaska to winter here in the Place of Refuge. Yellow-legged tidal dancer, bobbing in pools away from the dangerous edge, what do you want us to know about this story? Why are you here?

Hone ana ko leo e 'ulili e
O kahi manu noho 'ae kai
Kia'i ma ka lae a'o kekaha
'O ia kai ua lana malie

The voice of the 'ulili
Is soft and sweet
Little bird who lives by the sea
Ever watchful on the beaches
Where the sea is calm.

I watch the bird, so lightly perched on the rock by the sea, the 'ulili who has flown here all the way from Alaska, heavy enough to fall from the sky and drown in the waves, she made it. We are both bound here by gravity.

Soften, I hear. The heart is the way in. Stay small and watchful by the calm sea until you can be it, and when you struggle have compassion—until you can be it, too. Compassion for all—mothers and widows, chiefs and warriors, arrogant men, gossiping women, yearning daughters, and even the shark god who lost his son. And even the shark.

> Compassion for the killer
> who was made not born,
> Nanaue entangled in nets
> flipping his tail toward the water,
> obeying the body's call,
> desperate to live
> like us all.

> Soften, begin
> small and watchful
> by the calm sea,
> the rough water will come soon enough.
> For now,
> place hand on heart and breathe,
> here in this place
> this refuge.

After the bird's cry has faded, I stand and make my way back through Mordor, careful not to slip on the succulents. A small dark shape zips through the palm trees—must be a piglet. A man, thin and bald and a little stooped, is walking on my same trajectory as we approach the park gates. He is holding a leash and I see that the piglet, who has turned back toward us, is a little dog, a chihuahua. It dashes up to me and stops, looking up at me without barking. The man scolds it without acknowledging me and shouts its name, "Pele!"

I smile to myself, wondering if he has any idea what powers

he invokes every time he calls his tiny dog to him. I silently tip my head to the dog, and to the goddess Pele herself, and continue on, slipping through the barriers, though again there is no one at the guardhouse to stop me.

Behind me, I hear a park ranger confront the man about not having his dog on a leash. I can dimly hear him excuse himself by saying he's new here and didn't know the rules. Bless you, I think. Forewarned is forearmed? Nobody puts Pele on a leash.

Rain. I unlock the door and bend into the shelter of my Fit. The Stones are still blasting from my phone. I could have sworn I'd turned off the music.

Driving back up the hill to "Sympathy for the Devil," I realize Easter is this Sunday, which means today is Maundy Thursday, the night of the Last Supper, the night Judas betrayed Jesus to Pilate, who sent his soldiers to seize him in Gethsemane, the garden where he shared his last meal with his disciples.

> And I was around when Jesus Christ
> Had his moment of doubt and pain
> Made damn sure that Pilate
> Washed his hands and sealed his fate
>
> Pleased to meet you
> Hope you guess my game
> But what's puzzling you
> Is the nature of my game

What's my game? I don't know. I don't even know what the game is, but I've been playing it and I don't want to anymore. Not this game of betrayal that's so deep in our bones they barely remember compassion exists.

Every time we judge we betray ourselves.

Ke'oni says the fern of compassion, Laukahi Hou, tells us compassion means to attend first to *one's own suffering*.

Am I suffering? Everything seems like it happened so long ago, but yes, my life is lived more in the past than right here and now. This is a form of suffering. It's clear—I don't believe in my own goodness, my right to take up space in the world. My body feels like a burden. So many aches and pains. I don't deserve to be here.

I seek a path beyond the need for redemption. Exhausted, I turn off the light. Auku'u, the black-crowned night heron keeps vigil over my sleep.

CHAPTER 3
RIDING THE GEAR SHIFT DOWN

ʘ

T HIS IS NOT a memoir. If this was a memoir, I would tell you why I don't feel like I deserve to even be in my own body, to take up the space given to me by a boundary of skin and bones. I would strip naked in front of you, bare my soul as if you were my therapist, a priest, God with a capital "G."

But this is not a memoir.

What is this book then? Now and then I do share my story. Sometimes I will tell you about how I fell in love with Waipi'o Valley and a man who was raised by lo'i and river streams, of how he led me across his family's land, lured me with a waterfall, of how the entire valley seemed like it was waiting for rain to crack the treetops and the leaves turned inward to funnel the water before it even fell, pulling the clouds toward the valley's deep gulches.

Sometimes I will tell you of how he cleared a path before us with a cane knife, slashed java plums and banks of impatiens that didn't grow wild where I came from. I will pick up a guava from the ground and he will tell me not to eat it. "Worms," he'll say, throwing a rock at an orange so high in a tree I think it's a bird. I will leave my body only to have him hand it back to me, heavy with juice in his palm. When my teeth prick the white pith, flowers will lift their faces toward the clouds.

These are the things I would tell you if this was a memoir. I would tell you why I was reckless and bold, expose my innocence, my longing for love so desperate I was porous and anyone with snapping teeth and a fin on his back could see right through me. Water passed through my skin, and light. In those days I was beautiful and sometimes I glowed.

I was beautiful and sometimes I glowed. Why did no one love me? If this was a memoir I would make some educated guesses and tell you, but really I don't know. Anything I say would be assumptions and conclusions, the end of a story, when I want this book to be about the beginning, a new here, right now.

But I will tell you about how we climbed up the moss-slick rocks to the second pool at Nanaue Falls, and how when we reached the waterfall he told me when he was a kid he and his brothers used to hide one pool up and watch the hippie girls slide down naked. I will tell you when he said this I took off my clothes without comment and slid into the opaque water, thick as milk, jade green and without reflection, and that I knew someday I would write about it, that my life was a quest for poetry.

I *will* tell you how I swam toward the other side without looking back when I heard the splash behind me. I am the poet: Orpheus, not Eurydice. This is my song. I will tell you, waiting for the sound of his breath to let me know he'd surfaced, I pretended calm for as long as I could.

No human could go without breath this long. Right until the last second, I pretended calm, and how at the last second when I felt a shadow pass beneath me in the dark water, something that should have been impossible in this place barely touched by sunlight, my limbs locked, that somehow I remained floating above that dark within the dark, the deeper darkness underneath my locked body.

It was only a few seconds. And then it was over and he was laughing in my face when he saw the terror in my eyes, popping up on the other side of me. "The shark's my aumakua," was all he said. Without apology, he dove back under, slicing the water without a ripple and I followed him back to the moss-slick rock and—but this is not a memoir.

If I was a therapist I would tell you my trauma response was freeze, not flight and maybe you'd nod, but this is not a memoir. This is the poem I found and everything in it means something else. Maybe you will find yourself somewhere in one of these loops and this will be your story, too. It may seem like it matters to know why we think we don't deserve to take up space, to have a body, to walk on Earth, but knowing will not liberate us from shame. Only surrender will do that. So let go of your need for the straight lines of a story now and allow yourself to be carried to a wider circle than the one you now inhabit.

But this morning some of *my* story came back and asked me to tell it. That will be my criteria for what I will share with you, not my own desire to be witnessed or absolved.

It was clear when I arrived at Two-Step for my morning swim. It seemed like no big deal—I just wanted to sit on the corner of a picnic table bench to put my booties on before I walked over the lava to get in the water, but the local occupying one half of the table with cooler, cutting board, a large unsheathed knife, and a pit bull puppy curled up asleep in a t-shirt, was not pleased.

"I'm just going to sit here for a second to put my booties on," I said to him over my shoulder, feeling him bristle.

He said nothing and that probably would have been the end of our exchange if the puppy hadn't stirred, stretched, and then stumbled across the table to me. I reached out to pet her and she nuzzled my hand.

"Oh my god, she's adorable," I exclaimed like everyone ever when a puppy crawls in your lap. I expected my gushing to break the ice, but instead, he said in my direction without looking at me, "We try keep people from touching him."

What he really meant was, "Don't fucking touch him, stupid haole."

I felt like I'd been smacked in the face. I stood up, booties on, and walked back to my car.

"Stupid haole."
"Fuckin' haole."
"Stupid fuckin' haole."

I am 26 years old. There is no social media. The internet is a dream that doesn't exist yet. There are no cell phones. If you can't find a landline, you find a phone booth that takes coins for throwing your voice halfway around the world. If you don't have coins no one will hear you except the birds.

I am riding the gear shift between two local boys who picked me up at the Waipi'o Lookout. Down the almost vertical pali we go, straight down to the bottom of Waipi'o where in blind bravado I will pitch my tent under the ironwood pines by the beach. I have a plan. The boys think this is funny. There is no campground, no drinkable water, or store to buy it from. They make sure to point out the spot where their friend drove his Suburban off the pali at dawn returning home after an all-night bender. Later I will meet this friend and even spend a week trapped by floodwaters in his house he built from the ruins of the Peace Corps Training Camp that looks like something out of Swiss Family Robinson. I will learn that all-night benders can last all day, too, as in 24 hours, that people actually crack open beers in the blue hour while the rest of the party tries to sleep it off.

Riding the gear shift, bouncing down the pali, 26 years old,

I am acutely aware of their jean-clad thighs rubbing my bare skin. I let all thoughts drop beyond that and begin pitching my tent when we reach the beach. They offer to help and I say no. I can tell they are amused, but I will do this myself. When they ask me what I have to eat and I show them my plastic gallon of water, cans of tuna, and bag of granola, they laugh and say they'll bring me some more food tomorrow.

I have no plans besides eating, sleeping, and looking at the water. I am not exactly living in the moment. I'm aware the future exists, but I'm numb to it.

The next day only one of the local boys comes back. I will confess, expose myself—because sometimes this *is* a memoir— he is not "one of the local boys," he is the one with shark eyes who scanned me when I sat across from him at the lookout and saw I was easy prey, not because I was helpless, but because I *wanted* to be devoured.

He shows up with hands full of prawns and fiddleback ferns, and a pan to cook them in on a fire he builds. He shows me a spring where the water flows clean right out of the ground so I won't have to leave when the plastic jug is empty. He tells me stories.

He brings me to the spring. He tells me stories. I drink his words with the trust I lost as a child.

The stories are alive here, not fairy tales. When he tells me about the shark god and the girl who turned herself into a waterfall, he's telling me about his relatives. His family has been here that long.

The waterfall is named Hi'ilawe. The rocks beneath her are her lover who turned himself to stone to always feel her touch. The sound of her exultation is ever-present, she dreams me awake when I sleep until I can't tell the difference. She is always falling and now so am I, tumbling through the gulches to join the serpentine streams winding toward the ocean that will consume them. Drops obliterated. Only the thundering wave that rises up from tectonic plates to swallow the valley whole. The tsunami will come again. Everybody knows it. Land will give way to water and the only ones who'll remember are the stories.

Wild horses poke their heads in my tent, smelling granola. I read *Justine* from *The Alexandria Quartet* by Lawrence Durrell and *Midnight's Children* by Salman Rushdie, vintage editions from the used bookshop in Honolulu. I tear off pages as I read them, kindling. It's hard to start a fire in this dampness.

No WI-FI, No cell phone. No landline. No house. No electricity. No toilet (I dig a hole). I dine on wild ferns he brings me at dusk when he's pau work, walk to the spring to fill my plastic gallon, sit around campfires talking story with locals who come down for the weekend, drink Steinlagers and smoke joints, sing along to the guy playing guitar who says he played bass in Pure Prairie League. "Amie, what you wanna do? I think I could stay with you, for a while, maybe longer if I do..."

The shark boy tells me he loves me.

One weekend I decide to camp on the other side of the river. I find a spot just off the path where the ground looks soft, grass between big stones thrown about by a forgotten storm or god. There isn't quite room for my tent so my feet stick out on the path. There is still room for someone to pass. I have no problem falling asleep. By now I feel safe in the valley. I am young and foolish in my beauty.

ASLEEP IN THE RUINS

I needed to be held by grass,
sleep
with ear to earth, be sung
by underground water.

I needed to drink from the spring,
release gold spores with my breath
when I bent to the water,
bathe in the falls
lined in soft moss
green with primeval stories
from the time
when the valley was born,
lava collapsing a cleft
first covered in ferns.

Nobody told me
about the blood—
how the land craved it,
or how I would lose my will
in rain that washed away
riverbanks,
tearing out torch gingers
by the roots.
　　　Innocence

and ignorance, so close
in sound it's hard
to hear the difference.

I slept in the ruins
thinking they were only stones.

At the source of water
where ferns cast rippling shadows
water bubbled up
through unmourned blood.

Stupid haole, thinking I have the right to sit on the King's bench for my pathetic ceremony. I'd been too lazy to even remember his name when it was told to me. It's Keawe, by the way, and I apologize to his bones, wherever they are, for being so lame, and for all the tourists who sit on his stone seat. There's no sign not to, but sometimes you just know. That's the problem with haoles—we don't even know we don't know.

Stupid haole, sleeping in the ruins of the island's other Place of Refuge, Paka'alana, swept away by a tsunami. The grass between the stones was so soft... surely nothing could harm me?

Fuck that local who dissed me, I think, scrapping eloquence. It's Good Friday. Jesus is high on the cross and the sky is going dark on Golgotha. I've got work to do. It's time to head down the mountain and start over.

CHAPTER 4
SEASON OF THE WITCH

THREE WHITE cattle egrets cross my path from above, a triangle of silent seraphs, going up the mountain as I go down. This time, when I reach the park, I stride right over the speed bump past the unoccupied guardhouse carrying my gin in an old kombucha bottle labeled, "Synergy."

I keep on toward the Park pavilion, pass the bathrooms and gift shop, and mural, head down the ramp onto the gravel toward the gap in the Great Wall. At the first pond, I glance left for the night heron, but if auku'u is there, he's not visible.

I stop at the gap, acknowledge the four directions, and pour out a splash of gin without preamble. I don't hear a clear yes or no, so I just go. If I have to face a consequence for treading where I'm not supposed to, I'm willing.

A few steps in, my attention veers left to a pair of small pools. A rock bridge divides the water into bodies smelling of marsh muck and crushed succulents. My animal body is at home here.

One pond is larger than the other. I step onto the bridge between them and cross over. Where shall I sit? There's no solid ground to the right so I step left where my foot immediately sinks up to the ankle. I hop to solid rock, alarmed I'll be pulled under. Mud makes no promises. There's a nice, flat rock on the southern shore of the larger pond. I take a seat and pour out some more gin around myself in a circle.

This small, muddy pond, even the larger of the two, is a far cry from the King's bench with its epic view of Honaunau Bay. I can't imagine the King even noticed this place. There is nothing at all special about it. It's just a small pool, with about a twenty-foot circumference. At least it's filled with water; the right-hand pool is severely lacking the element that makes it what it is, parched and desiccated, pretty soon it will not be a pool, but a mudhole. *If this is the place for my ceremony, show me a clear sign*, I ask silently. Within a few seconds, the pond starts to ripple from within as if the water is moving itself. A cardinal lands on a shrub across from me, watches me for a half-minute, then chirps. It disappears into the sky the way birds do, a red flash for me to interpret.

Something side-shuffles out from under two small rocks in the water a foot from my seat. The rocks are propped against each other and make a little lean-to, just enough shade for a minnow to shelter from the burning sun. The creature's motion kicked up mud. When the water settles, I spy a small crab, just two or three inches of shell and waving claw, looking up at me from the stone shelter.

There is someone to hear my story.

"You want to hear a story, Crabby?"

"What's that, you say? Not Hi'ilawe?"

I'd been planning to tell the story of the tragic lovers of Waipi'o who became rock and waterfall, but looking at the jaunty crab looking up at me waving its bigger claw, Hi'ilawe seems too morose.

"Tragedies are all very well, but I hear you," I say. "I far prefer *As You Like It* to *King Lear*. I'm not in the mood for tragic lovers either. How about a story where a crab's the hero? Can you believe I know one?"

Crabby doesn't say yes or no, so I decide for him. Let's see if this fool can pull some magic out of thin air. Let's leap into the magician's hat.

THE NAME

Once upon a time there was an old witch who lived in a mountain forest. She was about as mean a witch as could be. Everyone stayed away from her, except for one poor spellbound girl she'd bound to her as a slave.

This poor girl worked day and night for the old witch, who didn't even feed her. One day, as the girl watched her mistress eating beans and rice, she dared to ask for some food.

"Why should I give you anything you filthy wretch of a girl!" Exclaimed the indignant witch.

The girl cringed and shuffled away.

"Wait," the witch commanded. "Tell you what. If you guess my name, I'll give you something to eat."

"But how can I do that!" the girl cried. "No one knows your name!"

"Not my problem," said the old witch.

That night the girl went to bed hungry and without hope. In the morning when she reported for work the old witch said, "I've a hankering for turkey intestines with my beans and rice today you worthless wretch. Take these guts to the river in the forest and rinse them off."

The girl gathered up the bloody, goopy guts and headed into the forest toward the sound of water. When she got there, she knelt on the bank and lowered the intestines into the water. She was so hungry she would have eaten them raw, but she knew the old witch would find out and she would be punished.

Suddenly, the head of an eel rose up out of the water and said to the girl, "Give me some of those intestines," flashing its sharp teeth.

"I can't," wailed the girl. Then an idea came to her. "I'll give you some if you tell me the old witch's name."

"I can do that," the eel agreed, so the girl tore off a bloody hunk and tossed it to the eel who snatched it in its wrist-crunching jaws and promptly disappeared back under the water.

Disheartened, the girl returned to rinsing off the intestines, worried the old witch would be able to tell a portion was missing, when what should happen, but a fish head popped above the surface and demanded the same thing. "Give me some of those guts."

The girl figured why not give it another try and repeated her offer. "I'll give you some if you tell me the old witch's name."

"Will do," said the fish, but as soon as he'd caught the intestines in his fishy lips he was under the surface with no flashing fins in sight.

The girl was really worried now because it was obvious a good chunk of the intestines were gone. There was no way the witch would let her get away from this, so her first reaction when a shrimp popped up and asked her the fateful question was to say, "No way!"

But then she remembered how the third time was so often the charm in all the stories she'd heard, and agreed to give the shrimp a share of the intestines in exchange for the old woman's name.

Alas, the shrimp was also a grifter and skulked off as soon as it got what it wanted, leaving the girl in utter despair. There was just a shred of intestines left, a mere scrap. The old woman would kill her, she was sure of it. She might as well throw herself in the river and get it over with. Thinking these dire thoughts, she noticed something out of the corner of her eye—a crab—walking sideways toward her out of the water.

"Hey, whadda ya got there?" said the crab. "Mmm! Is that bloody intestines? Give me a bite."

"A bite is all I have," said the little girl. "I'm doomed. You may as well have it. But first I have to ask, if I give this last scrap to you will you tell me the old witch's name?"

"Yes, I will," the crab responded, "sure thing. But you have to promise not to tell her I told you because otherwise, she'll kill me."

"Okay," she agreed. After being betrayed three times, she didn't believe him, but she tossed the last scrap toward the crab who caught it in his claw and started scuttling back into the water.

Just as the girl was about to give up all hope, the crab stopped and yelled back at her, "Her name is In A Storm Coffin On Your Back!" then disappeared under the water.

The girl leaped up and ran back to the cabin, bursting through the door breathing fire. The witch looked up, startled, from her meal of rice and beans.

"What's this? Where's my intestines?" she demanded.

"I know your name!" the girl shouted in triumph. And before the old witch could do anything to stop her, she hollered so loud the whole mountain heard, "In A Storm Coffin On Your Back!" And the spell that bound her to the witch broke. She was free.

The witch howled with rage, for it was true, In A Storm Coffin On Your Back was her name.

"Who told you my name?" she screeched.

"I'll never tell," the girl said, confident now that she was free.

Foaming at the mouth, the witch pieced it together. "It must have been someone at the stream! I'm going after them." Grabbing her cane knife off the wall she stormed out of the cottage toward the river. "Traitor! "You're dead meat! I'm coming for you!"

The girl sat down and enjoyed a huge bowl of beans and rice.

When the witch reached the river she railed at the eel who popped his head up to investigate the commotion. "You slimy bastard, did you tell that girl my name?"

"Wasn't me," said the eel, slinking quickly away.

Next came the fish, stuffed from his meal of turkey intestines. "It was you! Confess or die!" the witch shrieked.

"Not I!" insisted the fish, darting away upstream.

The same routine went down with the shrimp, and as the witch stood frothing at the stream's edge, who should appear but the crab. The old woman glowered and gave the real stink-eye.

"Did you tell the girl my name?" she growled.

"I did! It was me!" The jubilant trickster crowed. The witch was not impressed.

"I'll kill you!" she proclaimed, lunging toward his claws with her cane knife, but the crab just laughed, which enraged her even more.

"Bahahahaha! You'll kill me? Yeah, right! Just try it, old witch. See if you can get me!"

Enraged, the witch strode into the water. "I'll kill you!"

"Come get me!"

Back and forth they went, the crab moving steadily sideways into deeper and deeper water.

"You crusty wretch, I'll pluck your eyes out and suck out your innards!" she threatened, slashing the water with her cane knife, so sure of herself she didn't notice the water was over her head until she was drowning.

When it was over and she was dead, she sank to the bottom. The crab feasted, pulling her gizzard-fattened flesh from her bones while the water gurgled with laughter all around him.

The crab says come closer, come closer!
Better watch out witch
Your fire can't stand up
to that sideways scuttler,
magician of air and water
at home in the mud.
Glug, glug, glug
are the old witch's last words.
Betrayal is a bitch.
Who ended up with that big bowl of beans and rice?
Sometimes only the good *don't* die young.

When I finish, the crab is still looking up at me. I must look like Gulliver, a giant invader of his murk. To my right, motion. I turn and look. Water bubbles up through the bottom in the center of depressions in the pond. They look like the calderas of mini underwater volcanoes. We are too far from the ocean, about 400 yards, for this to be a tide pool. Where is the water coming from? An underground spring?

And there are fish! I didn't see them when I first sat down. They are a few inches long, drab-colored, though some have bluish lips and filament-thin red pectoral fins. They look like large goldfish or mini koi. One of them sticks its lips out of the water. "Little fish, are you blowing me kisses?"

Up my gaze roams to the most forlorn palm I've ever seen growing out of solid rock against the Great Wall that forms the far edge of the pond. It's tall but crowned with only a few scraggly fronds. No shade and certainly no coconuts will come from here.

Nowhere to hide. I'm just off the path tourists walk on their way through the park. Anyone will be able to see me.

They probably won't look. We're just a blip on the way to something bigger and better, a boring detour on the way to the real story. Anyway, I can't worry about being interrupted.

What can they do? I'm just sitting. No crime against sitting and I don't really care anymore if people think I'm odd. Crabby is still here. That's what's important. He has tiny antennae near his mouth that continually flutter one at a time, feeding himself something invisible to my eye.

What's that? Now that I'm up close I notice another crab, larger, wedged deep in the rock cleft. I wonder what you have to do to get that spot?

Gently, the water bubbles. A splash as one fish flits away from another. Another crab steps out from behind a rock to my right. The pond is going about its business as if I wasn't here, which pleases me.

My nose practically to the water, I notice the four-inch depression in front of me is swarming with tiny white snails, maggot-size mollusks crawling over each other. I'm tempted to pick one up, but don't, thinking of the Lilliputians.

A mynah watches me from the smaller tree. Have you been there the whole time, you imp? Why so silent?"

Mynahs are usually raucous, the colonial Hawaiian equivalent of crows, chatting away to each other. The endemic Hawaiian crow, 'alalā, is nearly extinct.

I stand up, almost step in the mud again, and notice: four large, long-toed bird tracks, unmistakably heron. *So, you've been here all along,* I think. *How could I have missed your tracks?* I'd been in such a rush to find my place I stepped right over them.

Back over the rock bridge and through the gap, and there he is, auku'u himself at the edge of the fish pond. He looks at me. No fear. He takes a few steps in my direction. *Thank you,* I bow, *good night and good hunting.*

CHAPTER 5
THE RATTLE OF BONES

TODAY I WALK the back loop into the park. It's not easy. The "path" is ankle-wrenching lava rock that ripples like the waves it once was, though if you trip and fall you'll find yourself sliced open instead of embraced. There is no give at all. You have to be as sure-footed as the goats who live back in this scrubby bushland bleating at the sun to traverse it safely.

It's Saturday, the day after Good Friday. Jesus is in the tomb. The Three Marys who wept at his feet while he died are outside the cave. It's the day we wait without hope, even though we know the end of the story.

But do we? Who guaranteed the Resurrection? God? Even if he did, I don't believe in him anymore. Not that I don't believe in something, just not that God with a capital G, who, though man is supposedly made in his image, seems so strangely anonymous. I need a God with a body, flesh and bones and flowing blood, someone like Jesus, but not the one we read about in the Bible. It's the apocryphal Jesus who makes my blood sing, the man who lay with Mary Magdalen by the shore of the Sea of Galilee and touches her with such tenderness the stars still weep. The man who gave his bones to Earth willingly, so that we can one day be redeemed, which in my gospel means to find the god within ourselves beyond gender, race, class, or even belief.

When I was 23, living in Washington, DC, I spent an afternoon walking around the city with a guy who'd grown up on a ranch in Arizona talking about what I thought was everything worthwhile: films, art, poetry. At the end of the day, clearly not impressed, he said to me, "Everything you know is from books."

I remember feeling insulted, but most of all ashamed. "How dare he mock me?" said one voice in my head. The other voice said, "He's right." I should have told him to fuck off, but I was so fragile at that age, permeable as pumice, light as a floating stone, I kept silent and internalized the shame. He was kind of right, but I let him make my innocence wrong. Shame was the driving force in my life.

Now I can see I was lacking what Martin Shaw calls "bone memory." In his words: "Imagine a laboratory with a little chick in it. They do these weird experiments with chicks. You've probably seen it where they put over the chick, the shadow of a pigeon, and the chick doesn't respond. You put the shadow of a hawk over the chick, and it shudders."

Bone Memory. I suppose what I was really lacking was access to it, because I, like you, have a whole skeleton of bones holding me up, and these bones are made of calcium, collagen, and blood-making marrow. I am self-made. I, like you, grew my bones out of the soft tissue granted by the union of my parents' cells. In my mother's womb, ignorant of light, my ancestors sang to me and I formed my bones in the shape of spiraling water. The opposite of a crab or mollusk whose shells protect their soft bodies, I, like you, made myself tender and exposed.

Flashback, 1994:

My boyfriend is done with work leading trail rides through the valley. We meet on the beach where the river is swallowed by the ocean's mouth.

I am lost inside my own world, overwhelmed with the sound of falling water. I don't notice the small group of people dressed in what look like togas walk past us until my boyfriend points them out.

"Those guys from da Sovereignty movement," he says. I had just learned there was a sovereignty movement, people who refused to acknowledge Hawai'i as part of the United States. They wade into the river and disappear into the ironwoods on the other side, and I don't think of them again until next day, visiting his mom up top, we hear on TV someone broke into the Bishop Museum in Honolulu and stole the ka'ai containing Chief Liloa's bones. The Sovereignty Movement claims responsibility. The ka'ai had been returned to Waipi'o.

It's the ka'ai I'm thinking about now as I pick my way across the lava. A forlorn goat bleats in the kiawe scrub. It's so dry this could be the Sinai desert if you didn't know the ocean was just over the hill. Jesus could have walked here with the disciples preaching at sunrise and resting under the shade of a palm until it was time to share wine and figs with his beloveds by the shore when the sun went down.

How long does it take before a place dwells in your bones? I remember hearing Martin say more than once that you don't really belong to a place until you've buried an ancestor in the local graveyard. What do my bones remember that I don't? That's one of the things I'm here to remember, spirits willing. I trudge on, looping back toward the passageway between the Great Wall that leads to my pond.

Why was this wall made in the first place? Standing before

the wide opening it doesn't seem like much defense. There is no give at all to the lava. Safe passage is only for the sure-footed, like the goats, and they may not be safe much longer. There is talk of rounding them up and eradicating them.

Flashback: Two months ago

Jada is on my massage table on the lanai at Paliuli Farm. We are perched on the hill above the ruined terraces where the maka'ainana grew kalo and sweet potatoes to feed King Keawe and the priests and chiefs down below at the Place of Refuge.

She has been ill, short of breath. She speaks of a breast lump but has never been diagnosed. No doctors. No poking and prodding, she insisted. Clear with her choice.

She melts into my hands, my palm on the back of her heart and when she turns over and looks up at me like a fawn discovered in a fern glade far from its mother, I tell her I love her.

"I love you, Jada."

"You have no idea how much I love you," she says.

Three days later she dies in Waimea Hospital from breast cancer.

Jada knew in her bones how to die like a cat that crawls off into a safe and secret space to concentrate all its force on leaving its body—the labor of death important as birth. She died with the focused bearing down of an animal who knows its sacred duty—to carry back all it learned in the light to feed the dark, to keep the balance. We were all shocked it happened so fast, but most of all I felt awe at her courage.

Bone memory. Knowing how to labor, to bear down through fear and pain, the absolute letting go so one can become an ancestor with grace, someone for others to call out to in the soul-making times when life trips you up and you fall on the sharp lava, so you can become someone for others to believe in.

Bones, preservers of mana—
Hawaiians hid them in caves.
The bones of great chiefs
sealed in ka'ai,
the woven baskets worshiped
right here in the Place of Refuge.
Chiefs' mana
guiding the people for eternity.

But so many bones
have been lost. Locked up
in glass cages,
hidden in drawers
in temperature controlled rooms,
never to be rattled by the wind
or polished by moonlight
warmed by the sun
or chilled in shadow.
Lost bones
nobody sings to.

I love you, Jada. My bones knew.

I walk through the gap and head left toward the ponds, stop at the stone bridge. There is less water today. Heron tracks erased—which means enough water came in during the past 24 hours to claim them. Tidal then, the pond. I could dip a finger in to taste it, but something has told me not to touch the water until I'm invited. I question this at first. It's not like I'm hearing some voice besides the one inside my head and I don't want to claim any special powers for myself that raise me above others, but I decide to trust that voice inside my head, even if it does sound like my own. *I can wait,* I tell the water.

The water is so shallow today, that in certain spots, the fish have to turn sideways to swim freely. Crabby, my companion from yesterday, is here in his rock fort and I notice another crab to my right hiding around the corner of a rock. Clusters of brown fish, females I presume, swim in place in the large center depression. The crab to my right pops its eyes above the surface to investigate me without the distorted prism of water. It filters something—food I assume— into its mouth with filmy claws in a steady rhythm. Eating the invisible—curious. Also curious, the tiny white snails from yesterday have evaporated. Gone. The only trace of their swarm, a few empty shells. When I shift my weight, the crab burrows into the mud.

Two male fish, slightly larger than the females and more colorful, swim toward me. I can see they have blue lips, dark gray bodies, and feathery red pectoral fins which they flutter to swim in place. As long as I hold still they don't seem threatened.

Something slices the water beyond the small school. There is a much larger fish in this pond, amazing considering how shallow the water. I watch it loop like a queen around the pond in figure eights. Here's a story for the Queen of this Pond:

THE BIRTH OF THE TITANS

In the very beginning of this adventure we're still having, the adventure of material existence itself, of being in a body, no one existed but Father Sky and Mother Earth. They have a lot of names, but in this story that bubbled up through a Greek mountain spring just after the beginning of time, they are known as Uranus and Gaia.

Now Uranus and Gaia were pretty enraptured with each other, and in the way of these things, made a lot of babies we know as the Titans. It's hard to imagine the Titans as babies, but they were once, just like you and me, only with bigger muscles and brighter teeth.

The stage was set to populate the earth, except for one thing: Uranus would not let Gaia give birth to their children. He wanted to keep the world all to himself without fear of ever being usurped. He wanted to be King, always.

Gaia wanted to see her children grow and flourish. She wanted grandchildren. Something had to be done. She came up with a plan to overthrow Uranus.

The plan involved a sharp sickle. The next time her husband came to lay with her, one of the unborn Titans would castrate him.

There was one hitch: none of the unborn kids were keen to do this. It wasn't so bad in Gaia's womb; they were safe and warm, but Chronos, the youngest, agreed to his mother's plot. He would do it. Space was a little tight. He would chop off his father's balls; castrate the King so he and his siblings could break free from Gaia's cramped womb.

That night when Uranus slipped into bed with Gaia, Chronos leaped out of her womb and castrated his father.

Back then nobody wanted a eunuch King. (Or now, as a matter of fact—machismo still reigns.) Uranus was easily deposed and his sickle-wielding son Chronos took the throne.

Chronos wasn't looking to reinvent the wheel with anything like polyamory or socialism. He took a wife, Rhea, and began to procreate, but his patriarchal impulses were even more draconian than his father's. He was an outright murderous dictator who killed his children and ate them as they slid out of Rhea's womb, until one day she couldn't stand the pain of carrying life only to see it devoured as soon as it breathed outside of her.

Just as Chronos was about to eat her latest son, she swapped the tiny babe's body for a stone. Bloodthirsty Chronos didn't notice and the baby grew in fast-forward speed to a young god called Zeus who slayed his father and became the new King, continuing the cycle of violence by raping, pillaging, and begetting children with goddesses and mortals all across Greece. I'm sure you've heard the stories. We're still living them.

But there's another river to this story, one not often remembered. Chronos, not the most loyal husband, cheated on Rhea with the enticing sea nymph Philyra. He had to change himself into a horse to hide from Rhea's notice, which is why Philyra gave birth to a centaur, the famed healer Chiron, half man/half horse. Chiron became a great teacher and healer who educated many young heroes: Achilles, Asclepius, and Jason all walked the mountain paths of his forest on Olympus. Being born of a god and a nymph, he was immortal, which never bothered him until Heracles mistakenly shot him with a poisonous arrow.

The pain was so unbearable Chiron offered to trade his life for Prometheus's freedom. Now poor, generous, noble Prometheus was being punished by control-freak Zeus for gifting fire to humans. The punishment was gruesome: chained to a mountain, eagles pecked and ate his liver, which continually regenerated. Zeus accepted Chiron's offer. Prometheus was freed and Chiron became the constellation Sagittarius.

Some say after being deposed by his son Zeus, Chronos, being immortal, set up shop in another blessed land and founded a new Golden Age that's still going on today. Some say he's still there ruling over it. Kind. Benevolent. White-bearded. Twinkly-eyed with wisdom and mischief.

Some say he faced his shadow and integrated his darkness. Some say when he looks over at us across the gap that separates our world from his, he weeps tears of true repentance, tears of remorse. But he can't do anything for us from there. It's up to us now. It's up to us to wake up and realize the blessed land could be here right now.

Back in the Place of Refuge the mysterious Queen processes on the pond's far side, weaving figure eights. The water is so shallow I worry she'll snag a fin or scrape her pearly belly, but I see no hesitation. She is all flash and muscle. The small fish swim sentinel.

Right in front of me, two of the small guys spasm and shudder with whole-body determination. They are spawning. I can't see the eggs she releases or his sperm, but desire is unmistakable. Here I am in my head and life is being created right in front of me.

The female fish swims back over the bowl's rim to the other females. The water is so shallow the male has to flip on his side to escort a new female back over the lip into his little bowl where the dance begins again, the shake and shudder. The Queen continues to loop, holding steady in the turbulence.

Bob Dylan pops into my head, *All I really want to do-oo, is baby be friends with you.*

This happens to me a lot in case you're wondering about all these songs that keep popping into this text like next door neighbors stopping by to borrow a cup of sugar. There's a jukebox inside me tuned to the Synchronicity Station. I pay attention.

I do want to be companions with these little fish—and Crabby and his cohorts fiddling under the rocks. Call me a dreamer, a Utopian, a romantic, whatever—I just want them to be excited each day at dusk when I come for a visit. Most of all, I don't want them to be afraid of me. I want them to trust this human.

When I try to stand up, my back seizes and it takes me five minutes to get down to the ground to pick up my backpack. On one knee, I smell the spicy resin of gin I poured on the rocks earlier. *Thanks for the reminder, Pele.* Stay humble. There is nothing special about what I'm doing. I'm just doing what humans are supposed to do, or trying. Just showing up, paying attention, and hopefully praising this little pond and its inhabitants with enough eloquence, that they know one human loves them.

The afterglow of sunset softens the Great Wall. The stones

absorb the light without any visible resistance. They will hold the sun's warmth for hours into the night.

Jesus is in the tomb. The Three Marys are wailing and waiting. What are they waiting for? Do they really need a savior?

Betrayal is an illusion, though the pain it creates is not.

Love the pain like the rainbow. Feel all the colors—even the spectrum we can't see, the ultraviolet, the infrared, the colors whose names we don't know.

Can we please just stop expecting Judas around every corner? Sacrifice doubt instead of lambs on the altar? Can we please stop feeding the children of Earth to war?

I cue up Dylan in the car:

> Now I ain't lookin' to compete with you
> Beat on, cheat on, mistreat you
> Simplify you, mystify you
> All I really want to do
> is Baby, be friends with you

CHAPTER 6
GOD IS A LIAR

◎

EASTER SUNDAY. Home writing this after a morning descent to the water.

Things I noticed at the pond today:

The water was a little bit higher.

The fish scatter at my shadow.

The circular sand depressions aren't made by underground springs, they are dug out by the little fish a mouthful of sand at a time.

Big Papa, the male who I've given another obvious and silly name, occupies the bowl right in front of my stone seat, defending his territory. Any intruder is summarily chased over the sand lip. He's willing to risk death for this. At one point when he flipped on his side to cross the shallow water he stranded himself and had to flop to get back in the water.

He's also a good housekeeper. I watched him push a leaf with his snout up to the rim a few times. He didn't have the strength to send it over the rim. When I left it had settled back onto the bottom.

The amorous couple to the left of Big Papa's territory were still going at it, waggling their tails and spewing sperm and eggs without shame.

Crabby crawled out to say hello. I enjoyed his perusal. He fled in a mud-flash when I lifted my hand to push my hair out of my face.

Last, but by no means least, there is a rainbow on this page. My pen is just about to cross it.

There, it's over. It disappears as soon as it hits the table and I am left again with a blank page. A blank page blessed by a rainbow.

> Easter Sunday—
> He is risen.
> The door is open.
> The three women at the tomb weep for joy.
> I hear them.

> The Three Marys—
> Mother, Sister, Wife
> fall to their knees and kiss his feet,
> sing alleluia
> when he steps through the door,
> light pouring forth
> from the hillside tomb.

> Il mare, La mer, El mar

Stella Mare
Star of the Sea,
they anoint his feet,
a libation of tears.

What if they were just human women?
What if nobody ascended into Heaven?
What if they all just died
or were happy to be regular people
doing the everyday things that bind us?

Look at them now—
braiding each others' black hair,
smoothing curls with oil.
One Mary rubs another's shoulders
while another Mary stirs lentils
on a fire that smells of myrrh.

After they've eaten
they lie on their backs in the desert
to watch stars blink out.
Nobody is sad about what they've lost
or afraid of what's to come.

In sickness, they tend each other,
and when the time comes,
wrap the well loved body
in a winding sheet, linen
crisp and smooth as a breeze
on a morning marsh.

Death arrives on minor chords,
the marrow's primal song
they've been silently humming since birth.

Weep and be made whole again by the river,
they tell us.

God is a liar—not a lie. That is what the rainbow told me when it
crossed my notebook page. That boy who walked the DC streets
with me all those years ago was even more right than he knew.
Not only was most of what I knew from books, most of it wasn't
true. Distorted by history's political agendas, God became a
tool to oppress, not liberate or love. God is oppressed, too. But
God is not a lie, even with a capital "G." There is a creator at the
source. I just know it. There is no pronoun able to encompass
God, no way to express that really rings true besides alluding
to what lies beyond the senses, the space created when Jesus
walked out of the tomb. In the meantime, I can do my best to
reclaim what I can of a history that no longer serves us. Here's
a story for that, Crabby and Big Papa.

THE RAPE OF MEDUSA

Ironically, I wasn't born a monster—though my sisters were.
Our parents were the sea nymphs Phorcys and Ceto and they
called us the Gorgons, three hideous girls and one beautiful—
me. My hair was exceptionally eye-catching, shiny copper ring-
lets to my waist. I was so gorgeous I caught the eye of Poseidon,
God of the Sea, and he raped me. There's no other way to say it.
I won't ask for your forgiveness for not sparing you the details.
If you don't want to hear it, stop reading. One afternoon I was a
virgin in Athena's temple, by evening totally depraved. Not the
way you think, not because I liked it. I was depraved because
Athena said so. Raping me, Poseidon desecrated her temple.
Guess who took the blame? I was the one she punished. In a
flash of lightning I can still feel shuddering through my body,
she changed my lustrous, copper hair into writhing snakes. My

heart turned to stone that day, and soon after anyone who met my gaze did, too.

I would still probably be turning people to stone if it weren't for the hero's quest, which obliged young men to go out in the world to prove themselves so we could all pretend this wasn't a shit life. A lot of heroes had tried to kill me. This one was different. Perseus was his name. Not only was he actually truly noble and not just a buffoon trying to puff himself up to get laid, he had the help of a whole bevy of my relatives, which is the only way he defeated me. Hades gave him a Cape of Invisibility, he got winged sandals from Hermes, and a sword from Hephaestus. But it was the bronze shield from Athena that did me in. Perseus knew he'd be turned to stone if he faced me, so he tracked my reflection in Athena's child and slashed my head off while I was sleeping.

> He killed my reflection.
> That wasn't me.
> But I am dead.
> If I am dead, who is this speaking?

I had children. That's what almost no one remembers. Poseidon knocked me up. I carried them for so long I forgot I was pregnant, too. I was hoping if I forgot them they'd just go away, my children of rape, but that's not the way the body works. It has a life of its own despite our desires, ironic since desire is what drives the body. My children's names were Pegasus and Chrysaor. They spilled out when Perseus slashed my throat, born on a venomous blood spurt. He was shaking in his boots so badly trying not to look at my dead head still writhing with snakes he couldn't lift his sword to kill them, too, so they escaped. I watched them with my many eyes as the blood surged out of me. The marble floor was slick and Perseus stumbled when he stooped to lift my head. They don't show that in the movies.

If Perseus hadn't cut my head off they could still be inside me kicking to get out or stabbing me with a spear that could have eventually punctured my guts. But Perseus did slash my throat, and despite how it looks in the movies, one clean sweep of the blade, he had to hack through my spine to separate my head from my body. Maybe that's why Chrysaor grew up to be a great warrior with a golden sword, although that doesn't explain Pegasus, who was so noble and beautiful everyone wept when he flew over them. Pegasus, the white-winged horse came from me. Hard to believe, right? I wouldn't have believed it if I hadn't watched him stand for the first time on his thin, shaky legs with the eyes of a hundred dying snakes.

Perseus flew off with my head and into many other lives. Everybody knows from "Clash of the Titans" how he used my head to rescue Andromeda by killing the kraken sent by Poseidon because he was pissed off that Cassiopeia, her mother, had boasted that her daughter was more beautiful than the Nereids. As if! And few people know the part about how when we flew over Libya on Pegasus snakes sprang from the drops of my blood that shattered on the desert sand, and that's why to this day, Libya is infested with snakes. But not many know the part of my story that gives me the most satisfaction. When Perseus finally made it to Athena she finally acknowledged what she'd done to me, in her own calculated, cool-hearted goddess way. She set my head in an *aegis*, which you probably know as a shield, that she gave to her father Zeus. So there I was protecting Zeus's heart. And Athena's sometimes, too. She liked to borrow the shield because, even in death, my gaze could slay. Athena could protect herself and kill at the same time when she carried me.

Athena did something else that pleased me. She didn't just send a slave in to mop my blood off the marble. She had her slave collect the blood in a vial and gave most of it to Asclepius, the god of healing, and from what I'm told, he used the blood from my left side to take people's lives, and the blood from my right to raise people from the dead. The last two drops she gave to her son Erichthonius. I don't know if he ever used them, but it was said one was a cure-all, the other a deadly poison.

Not many remember Erichthonius, probably because he doesn't exactly have a hero's name like Perseus or Hercules, vigorous and easy to pronounce, and what I'm going to tell you about him is going to weave my story with Athena's in a way that may surprise you, and perhaps make you think differently of how harsh she was to me after Poseidon raped me.

Most people don't know Athena had a son because she tried to hide it. But it's hard enough to hide a human, let alone a demigod, and Erichthonius was actually born of two gods, so there are no halves about it. He was born when Athena, wanting some new weapons, went to visit Hephaestus who was so overcome by lust he tried to "seduce" her. Athena fled, not just to save her virginly reputation, she was seriously repulsed by Hephaestus's hot paws on her breasts. She wanted nothing to do with him and was absolutely horrified when he came on her leg. Disgusted, she wiped off his spunk with a wool scrap like millions of women since and flung it to earth. Of course, being a god, the filthy seed couldn't just seep into the soil, it had to sprout into a son—voila!—Erichthonius. Athena wanted to abandon him, but couldn't. Even the cool-hearted goddess found that she had feelings when faced with her own son. Instead, she hid him in a small wooden box and gave him to the King of Athens, making him swear he'd never open it.

Well, we know how that goes.

The king held off, but his daughters couldn't.

Some say when the daughters opened the wood box they saw an infant with a snake coiled around it, some a creature half-child, half-snake. What everyone agrees on is the three sisters went mad at the sight and threw themselves off the Acropolis, and that this was the end of their story, though not of Erichthonius, who somehow grew up to be a normal-looking King of Athens who married Praxithea, a naiad, and begot a son, Pandion, who taught his people to smelt silver and till the earth with a plough, and how to yoke horses to a chariot, which is quite a coincidence since I know Jennifer had no idea who he was when she started writing my story today. This whole narrative she's concocting for you to read is moving through the Major Arcana right on schedule. Fool, Magician, High Priestess, Empress, Emperor, Hierophant, Lovers, have been chanting here in the background, and today the Chariot's wheels have rattled into this story.

Have you ever seen the Chariot card? The prince (who looks a lot like Athena), stands crowned and ready to battle in his chariot, pulled by a black sphinx on the left, a white on the right.

Have you ever wondered why life is so hard? Why for every one step forward there are at least two back? Yet somehow we all keep going. Willpower they call it. Determination. Erichthonius had it. He was such a competitive charioteer in the races, Zeus raised him into the sky to become Auriga, the constellation of the Charioteer. He's still up there lashing his sphinxes, one black, one white. Poison, antidote. Poison as antidote. I wanted to hate Athena's son, but he was part snake. It would be like hating myself, and I have suffered too much for that. And though Athena has never apologized for punishing me for being raped, in her own way she has acknowledged me. They say the snake behind her symbol is her son, but I know it's also me.

I know my story has been distorted and you probably think I'm a monster. Do I want to change your mind? I don't know. Do I want you to stop being afraid of snakes and lopping off their heads with machetes? Yes. I can say yes to that. What do I really want?

I have to stop and think about that. No one has ever asked me.

I never thought to ask myself.

What I want is to be remembered as an ancestor—for I am. I am a mother. I brought life into this world, not just terror, and my children's heroism and grace still inspire people today. And here's, to my mind, the most gratifying part of this story: not many know Pegasus gave birth as well, not to a mini flying horse, but to a holy spring on Mt. Atticus. When his hooves touched down on the slopes a spring burst forth. Hippocrene. Holy water flowed down Mt. Atticus and inspired the Muses. I am the grandmother of poetry.

CHAPTER 7
EMOTION IN MOTION

◎

WIND DRIVES my head between my knees. My stone submerged, I find a small patch of dry rock and crouch in my bone cave. Sights fall away easily as if they've never existed. The world is the wind whipping the waves onshore and the clack of palm fronds. The burbling coo of a mourning dove penetrates the evening. After a while, I lift my head and see two little crabs have approached. They gaze up at me with their eyes above the water. It's a very Gulliver and the Lilliputians moment. Would they bind me and transport me to their kingdom if they could? Big Papa and his cohorts float in place in their respective amphitheaters. Nobody seems anxious about my presence, but I know they will scramble in a moment if I move.

I sit for a long time, mesmerized by ripples, and begin to sing. *I lean my back up against a tree. I thought it was a trusty tree, but first it swayed, and then it broke, and so my false love did unto me.*

My ancestors sang this song. No one told me this, but my bones know it. Ancestors who'd once roamed Britannia's shores gazing into pools, colder than this one, crisp and metallic like the slate-gray Atlantic, dark and mystical, a different kind of invitation—to cross its labradorite waters, to risk everything for the New World. Their ships did not go down. They made it across and now I am here singing my melancholy to an audience of small, amorous fish and two crabs. The crabs wave their claws at me. Applause or an order to cease and desist? I don't know. I'll sing anyway.

> The water is wide
> I cannot get o'er
> And neither have I wings to fly
> Give me a boat
> That can carry two
> And both shall row
> My love and I
>
> I leaned my back
> Up against an oak
> I thought it was a trusty tree
> But first it swayed
> And then it broke
> And so my false love
> Did unto me

It's time to drop the pose. I've been alone too much. Untouched, I am lost in longing, tuned to memory instead of the present moment where I haven't had a human lover in years. It feels shameful to write that, like there is something wrong with me, that I'm undesirable when I know I'm not. The mirror I'm holding up to me is my own, the judgments mine, though they are sourced from terror and abuse, the words that slashed my self-esteem like shark's teeth. I learned that when one broke off, there would be another—rows upon rows of teeth, teeth like soldiers that slid into place on the front lines when their comrades fell. But how was I the enemy? There is much I haven't told you.

I descended into the valley. I fell in love. If this story was a comedy we would have married as Shakespeare's lovers do. If it was a tragedy, one of us would have killed ourselves or been killed. Maybe both of us.

We didn't marry. Obviously, I haven't been killed or killed myself. If my love story is not a tragedy or a comedy, what kind of story is it?

But first, let me tell you about the first time I gleaned this might be a tragedy I was in, not the comedy I longed for. We were seated in the passenger seat of the car he'd borrowed for a night of revelry up top of the valley. I don't remember what we were bickering about, but when I said I was getting out of the car his arm whipped across my windpipe pinning me to the vinyl: I froze.

I didn't fight back, not with words, certainly not with my fists. Doing nothing was the only action of which I was capable. I didn't even question it in my mind.

And I didn't question it in the days to come back down in the valley when the twin bed with creaky metal springs pushed against the wall in the corner became my place of refuge. On my side, facing the wall, I trained myself to disappear. If I didn't move on the outside, if I drew all my terror so deep inside my mind I couldn't feel it, numbed my body's impulse to flee, I became invisible to the shark patrolling the reef just a few feet away from me—the man between me and the cabin door. Even if I made it out, I'd have to cross so many rivers, walk a thousand feet up the road so steep I could almost touch it without bending over. To flee would provoke pursuit and I knew I wasn't fast enough. And what would I do when I escaped? The shame of it was too much. Numb to my reality, I chose to risk death than reveal how weak I was. The depth of my self-hatred was unfathomable to a normal person, the kind of person I thought worthy of love. I bet it all on surviving just one more night. It was always OK in the morning. Somehow I still had faith in the day when the sun rose.

Writing this, I realize how much shame still shapes the way I interact with the world. Here in the present, instead of feeling alone, the breeze coming down the mountain at dusk could be my lover, or the currents that swirl between my legs when I tread water in the great blue bay—if I could accept their touch. I imagine I am not the only human that feels this way, but as I write this, it becomes clear that I am choosing isolation, the withdrawal of my senses, the primacy of my thoughts that romanticize a past that was actually filled with horror, where desire—not just lust, but the primal need of a wounded child to feel safe and loved led me to the edge of death, the shark-boy's jaws at the river's mouth.

Now you've seen what's on the other side of the mirror, and yes, despite the terror, some of the images are so beautiful they still entrance me. Victimhood is confusing. You can do all the spiritual bypassing in the world, tell yourself your soul chose the horror in order to deepen and grow, and that may even be true, but the body, the magnificent, sensing body whose skin longs to be touched, doesn't understand the difference between a tragedy and a comedy, it just wants to merge. The body is an animal, so repressed in our culture. I unleashed it, my body, wanting the comedy's end, to marry and live happily ever after. Because I didn't die at the end, my story is not a tragedy. It's a third way—a bridge made of reality brutal as flint. Suffering *does* deepen the soul. Beauty always contains suffering.

THE BATH

He knows what I want at sunset
after we've worked all day in the taro patch.

As coolness from the deep gulches
rises up to claim the valley from the sun,
without words he chops wood,
while I fill a five-gallon bucket from the stream,
lift it over my head with shaking arms
to fill the fifty-gallon cistern.

Soon the fire is flickering, metal hot to touch.
Inside, the water sighs, changing form
without resistance, while the night-blooming jasmine
begins to release the moon's untouched longing.

I wait, watching the jacaranda burst
like a purple firework backlit above the cats
congregating on the front porch preparing to hunt,
move into the gloaming when they do
toward the bathhouse.

We take off our clothes together.
Waterfalls sprout like fresh ginger shoots
pouring down the valley walls to anoint us
with the blessing of holy lovers heard in the wind
moving through java plum trees.

I lower myself into the sunken tub first
while he stands above me naked.
He has the glistening belly of a fish
and when I meet his eyes I see
the boy his mother told me about
constantly tugging on her ear.
Listen to me.

I push myself up and take him in my mouth without

lowering my eyes.
        Legs interlocked,
we soap each others' hair with awapui
growing right next to the tub,
and rinse our heads with buckets of water.

The mud from the taro patch stains our palms,
outlines our lifelines and all the paths
we could take, but for now we are
two lovers breathing through mud
like the frogs chanting outside the open door
inhaling the canopy of taro leaves,
carried upstream and
down, lost in a whirlpool
where we give ourselves
to the spiraling water.

He massages the balls of my feet;
fingers trace feathered-arches.
The bird-like bones sing in his hands.

Beauty is holy. There is no shame in being mesmerized by it. Love contains all and holds space for shame as well as dignity. Forgiveness spans the gaps between shame and love like spider silk spun from our own bodies, and when it's time for us to weave again, our webs will be all the more beautiful because of our suffering. They will shine with tears at dawn and break the fall of the wounded. They will bless the fall—our webs, woven from silk inside our own bodies.

I am still here. My ancestors are listening. I stand up and hopscotch over some dry rocks to the bridge between the two ponds. For some reason I look back—the light is gold and glorious—the wind that pushed me inward, deep into the bone cave where my ancestors had been waiting for me, has sheared the few fronds left off the top of the taller palm tree. They have fallen to rest on top of the Great Wall that is unmoved by the wind. With the few fronds, the tree had looked somewhat alive, without them it's just a bare trunk pointing toward nothing. Eventually, it will fall into the pond and maybe a ranger will come and drag it away, or maybe it will be left to rot and the crabs will hide under it from the people passing by who don't realize the crabs know the witch's name.

A rain veil rises up the mountain from the sea.
The afternoon softens.
What can be seen behind the sun?
Petals, without shame, opening wider, wider—

Drops land whole on leaves and rest for a few seconds
before rolling along green veins to the next surrender.

Supine on the daybed,
I listen to the rain tap-dance on the roof.
I am serene, aware
of my own contentment.

When rain falls uphill
we go back to the beginning.
The story reverses,
the other side of the veil exposed.

Now we are the hidden ones.
Let us give up the search for our meaning.

SEDNA

I was born on the spring ice. First thing I heard: moaning and cracking, and the churning, great white paws of polar bears swimming across open water, claws out. As I slid into this world onto a blood-soaked sealskin, my mother slipped out of it. Nobody mentions that part of the story. As far as anyone knows I appeared as a fully formed rebellious teenager giving my father shit by refusing to marry the "suitors" he started foisting on me as soon as I started to bleed.

Maybe it would have been different if I'd had a mother. Who knows? I guess there's no point in having regrets, but I do. I wish my father hadn't said he was going to force me to marry the latest moon-eyed slobbering hunter who appeared at our igloo. I wish I hadn't run away and "married" the village scum, Dog-Boy, in an attempt to punish my Dad. Things could have been way different. But they aren't, so I just have to deal with it. We all do. Living in the Arctic helps. Surrounded by the frozen.

Dog-Boy was not frozen. He was hot as the steaming piles of shit he left all over the village. I'd been eyeing him since I was a little girl, curious about this boy who had the opposite story as me, a mother but no father. Nobody knew who his father was. His mother wouldn't tell. Most likely he was a wandering hunter, but because she wouldn't tell, we made up stories in the way villagers do, dooming the poor little boy whose name we didn't even bother to know. "Slut." We called his mother. "She was hungry for it. Nobody would marry her. She fucked one of the sled dogs, you know. That boy's father was a dog. That's why he shits wherever he wants."

Dog-Boy did not know he was shitting where he wasn't supposed to, so it was easy to conclude he was procreated by a dog, although the dogs were cleaner. He probably could have learned to control himself, but his mother, after giving birth to him in such disgrace, slipped into another world, though still in the same body that had given birth to him. She barely fed or washed herself, let alone her son, and would not have survived if her mother hadn't taken pity on her and left whale meat at the opening of her igloo.

There was not enough meat for the both, and Dog-Boy's mother, crazed and ashamed, did not share it. He was left to fend for himself, and since none of the villagers would take him in, he learned from the dogs, who eventually began to share bone scraps with him so that he didn't starve. He even slept with them, huddling in the pack to keep warm. Everyone thought he was crazy, but I came to know he actually believed he was a dog and didn't understand his shitting wherever he wanted was a problem.

He also had the instincts of a dog to hump and rut. When puberty hit this became a problem. You can imagine. Irate fathers and outraged mothers decided they were going to have to kill him once he started accosting their daughters. He was so horny and without self-judgment, he even humped some old granny's legs and once knocked down a bow-legged hunter and mounted him before some women who heard his cries dragged him off. You couldn't really get much lower.

I could. And that's what I did when my father insisted I marry his chosen young hunter from yonder. I stormed out of the igloo and ran straight to the dog pack on the edge of the village. "Dog-Boy!" I yelled. "Marry me!" Dog-Boy had no idea what marriage was, but he did know how to fuck, which is exactly what we did, ruining my reputation and my marriage prospects in one thrust.

It did not last long, though at the time it felt like it went on forever. My virgin blood stained my sealskin pants. The smell of it crusted on my legs did not repulse the Dog-Boy, it aroused him further. Pretty soon I was sleeping in the middle of the dog pack with him and growling when he mounted me. Pretty soon I was enjoying the neck nips and the way his tongue slobbered all over me. Pretty soon I was growling and nipping and slobbering myself, even turning over on my back sometimes when he fucked me, which shocked us both when our eyes met and we remembered for a few moments we were humans, not dogs. His shock shifted to wonder and I think he would have stayed like that looking deep into me, but I flipped over and thrust my ass toward his eyes and the dog rose up in him again, dominating, and our chance to regain our humanity melted away like spring ice.

As long as I could forget being human, it wasn't bad being a dog. I slept in the pack so I was never cold and Dog-Boy started stealing the whale meat left out for his nearly comatose mother. Once my father stood outside his igloo and called me. "Sedna!" he yelled with such anguish I almost ran back home to him with my head between my tail, but I resisted. I was ruined now. No one would ever marry me. My only choice, if I went back, would be to live the rest of my life as his servant. I'd rather die fucking and the smell of shit no longer bothered me.

And that would have been my history if one of the other dogs hadn't taken an interest in me. I'd slept so long with the pack I no longer smelled like a human. Poor Dog-Boy, my lusty, devoted husband had no chance against the blue-eyed alpha who ripped his throat out before he could mount a defense. I know he would have, and I've always remembered that look between us when I flipped on my back with my spread legs and faced him. I wasn't ready yet to fuck an actual dog, so when the alpha came for me I fled. I glanced over my shoulder once and saw him tearing into my mate. I should have been sad, but I couldn't really feel anything any more, not since I'd heard my father call my name into the dark night. No more pain. I understood why Dog-Boy's mother never left her igloo, even if I didn't know the details of her story.

The villagers all wondered what had happened to Dog-Boy, but I didn't tell them. For three days I walked past the pack and watched them gnawing his bones, and then they were gone. I no longer smelled like a dog because my father had taken me back. He'd rubbed me down with snow, not saying a word about the dried blood between my legs. For a time there was peace between us, but eventually, he started up with his plans to marry me off. At the time I thought it was his pride, but I think he may just have wanted grandchildren. A part of me wishes I could have given him what he wanted, but I wasn't born to fulfill his life.

Of course, defiled as I was, no one in the village would marry me. My father had been pretending nothing had happened. His talk was all about how one day I would marry a great hunter and have my own igloo and he would come to visit me on his sled and play with his grandchildren. I was not ashamed of what I'd done with Dog-Boy, but I didn't have the heart to disillusion my Dad. Let him believe what he needed. When I looked at him in the light coming down through the smoke hole I saw more gray hairs on his head every day. Sometimes his voice shook, and once his hand slipped when he was scaling fish and almost sliced off his index finger. He was not pointing it at me. His rage was spent. I was too sad to blame. So I said yes when the strange, cloaked hunter came to our igloo and asked to marry me. My father was overjoyed and even planned a wedding feast. I knew no one would come since I was the village disgrace, but I went along with his plans. Maybe my father would be so deluded with delight he wouldn't notice no one had joined in on his toasts.

Did I ask my husband to reveal his face under that cloak? No. I never wanted to meet a man's eyes again. He could have my body, this cloaked man, but not my heart. That would remain frozen, not even thawing in spring when the polar bears swam across the melted ocean.

My new husband didn't touch me. He must want to wait until we're alone, I thought to myself, though nobody in the village ever had much privacy. Having to live in igloos to survive, we generally humped in full view and sound of each other, though under furs and sealskins. Nobody took it out in the open like Dog-Boy and me. The last thing I remember is the sound of my father snoring and a greasy finger parting my lips and pouring a liquid that tasted like dark berries and caribou dung onto my tongue. I gagged and tried to spit it out, but the finger became two hands that clamped my jaws shut. I swallowed and then I was gone, descended into blank space.

I expected to wake up wrapped in furs. Instead, I found myself in my tattered, stinking seal skins in a giant nest built in a crag on a thousand-foot cliff above the churning ocean. My husband was perched on the rim, and when I saw him I understood why he'd never removed his cloak. He was a giant, greasy, squawking fulmar. "Not what you expected, eh wife?" he laughed, snapping his giant beak.

"How did I get here?" I cried out in horror, scrambling to the far side of the nest until my back was against the cliff wall. A thousand feet of rock above me, another thousand below to the sea. There was no way out except for growing wings or leaping. Looking down, I knew I would never survive the leap. "You flew," my new husband informed me. I checked my back. Had I spouted wings? Was I going to be able to flee this nightmare? He laughed and dashed my hopes with his next words, "I gave you a sleeping potion on our wedding night and grabbed you by the back of the neck with my beak. You can try to escape, but you know where that leads."

Far below I could hear the waves crashing on the rocks. "Please, take me back to my father!" I pleaded. "Never, my dear. I've been waiting a long time for a wife. Believe it or not, nobody would have me. I finally found someone desperate enough to give his daughter away."

"Did my father know?" I asked in horror. Was this his punishment for my refusal to obey and for defiling our family name? How could he do this to me? He wouldn't even get grandchildren out of me because, unless a miracle occurred, I couldn't lay eggs, even if the fulmar and I did manage to mate. "Why, Father!" I sobbed to the sky.

"Save your voice, he can't hear you," my new husband scolded me. "Nobody likes a shrill woman. Not even a fulmar. And yes, of course, your father knew, though we didn't talk about it. Who else would take a daughter who had defiled herself with a shit-smeared dog?"

"He wasn't smeared in shit!" I protested. "He just acted like a dog because nobody loved him. Except for me!" And with that I burst into inconsolable tears, thawing tears that burst my dammed heart and reached my father's. "Sedna! I'm coming!" I heard in my mind from far, far away.

I settled into my corner of the nest and pretended to submit to the monster I'd married. He left me alone for most of the day, soaring over the waves to hunt, returning with raw fish he fed me from his beak. I had to open my mouth and let him stuff it down my gullet. I gagged but got it down. I had to keep up my strength. My father was coming for me. It was bitterly cold in the nest. My husband was warm in his water-proof feathers, but I had nothing to cover me. If my father didn't come soon I would freeze to death. "I can keep you warm," he cackled, lifting his wing and nodding at me to come over.

"I'd rather die!" I spat. He was not offended, on the contrary. It gave him more opportunity to mock me. His sheen waxed the more desperately I pleaded, and I did plead. I had no pride left and would have gladly married a normal village man if one would have still taken me.

"I can't give you children," I reasoned with the fulmar.

"I don't care. I'd push them out of the nest anyway."

"I'll never love you."

"Hate me please. It only makes me soar."

"I fucked a Dog-Boy for 1,001 nights."

"I'm a porn freak. You're making me horny."

"That's bestiality."

"My fetish exactly. Are you into BDSM? You're giving me a boner."

"I'll cut off your dick like Loreena Bobbitt!"

"Ha ha ha ha ha!" he howled. "I don't have one. But if you want to scrape your knife along my cloaca I'm into kink!"

At that I gave up, hunching into myself like a dying polar bear. Maybe my father was coming. Even if he was, I didn't think I'd make it.

He came at dawn in his kayak, crossing the dark water as my husband flew off to hunt. My relief when I looked down out of the nest and heard his voice booming up at me—I can't even find the words for it. My father had come. He loved me after all. My broken heart strained from holding in years of tears, exploded in sobs of grief and relief that rained down on my father's kayak. "Sedna! I'm here! Stop crying!" He shouted up. I gasped for breath, trying to calm myself. He loved me.

"Listen," he shouted. "I can't climb up there to get you. The rock face is too sheer. You're going to have to leap." The gravity of this reached me through my tears and I looked down at him as my eyes cleared. There was a thousand feet between us. If I missed the kayak where my father would catch me, I'd drown or be smashed to bits on the rocks. How could I do this? I didn't have the courage. Then I thought of my fulmar husband's greasy stink, and of how his depraved thoughts had already wormed their way into me and further tarnished my already bitter heart. Without hesitation, I stood up and stepped off the nest rim, arms out like wings.

Maybe I had invisible wings. Maybe my unknown mother's spirit was watching over me. Maybe it was Dog-Boy's ghost breaking my fall by the ankles with his teeth. Somehow I made it safely into my father's uplifted arms without knocking him out of the kayak, sending us both to sure death in the Arctic. Wrapping a fur around my emaciated bones and tucking me between his legs, my father turned the kayak and headed back across the ocean toward the village on the ice I'd once hated, but could now not get back to fast enough. Homeward bound. My blood sang.

My father did his best. He was a strong paddler, but the waves were against him. He had spent years getting to know their ways, but my fulmar husband *belonged* to them, winging over the crests and into the peaks day and night. When my husband discovered his plaything had escaped, he summoned a storm and the wind and waves obliged him, batting our kayak about like two battling walruses. "Sedna, you filthy whore! Dog fucker! I own you! There's no escape!" he shrieked into the wind. His great wings beat the air like a gong, rippling and distorting our vision. The air churned as much as the water. We couldn't tell up from down. "Father!" I screamed, turning back to reach for him so that he'd know I loved him too as I was thrown out of the kayak.

I'll never forget the look in his eyes. It pierced through my furs and froze and burned simultaneously until I was nothing but a loosely bound bundle of bones tied together by cartilage that rattled in the wind when he lifted me over his head and threw me into the waves. "Take her!" my father screamed to my husband, who shrieked in triumph as he finally caught up with us, plunging toward me to peck out my eyes. "You'll pay, Sedna," he screamed. "You'll pay!"

My father had thrown me over. He wanted to live more than he loved me. I wanted to die now so he would get what he wanted. I would make it easy. I would not be the fulmar's wife.

I don't know if it's because I was wearing a sealskin, but when I let go and tried to slip below the water, it wouldn't take me. I kept bobbing up while the fulmar circled above trying to grab onto my hood so he could lift me above the waves. I don't know why my arms shot out of the water and grabbed onto the gunwale of my father's kayak, or why the word propelled itself out of me, "FATHER!" I yelled into the wind through a mouthful of seawater.

What did my father see looking down at his daughter's hands clinging to the gunwale in the worst storm he'd ever seen? Did he see a filthy whore daughter who'd disobeyed him and fucked like a dog in full view of the village, shaming him forever? Did he see his wife's blood on snow and sealskin as I slipped from between her legs as she died in a hot gush that branded me forever with the weight of blame?

I never learned, and I never saw him again. I still don't think I could find the words to ask him, even though a thousand years and more have passed. I still have a hard time describing how he looked *at* me, not away, so his aim would be sure. How he raised his paddle above his head and clubbed my frozen fingers clinging to life, despite wanting to die. I shattered like a baby seal's skull.

I let go for the second time that day, first the leap, and now this, sinking, sinking, sinking. At first, I didn't realize I had no fingers, but when I looked around me and saw eels and dolphins and narwhals and every manner of fish you can imagine, I noticed the ghost pain and looked at what had once been my hands. My father's club had snapped my frozen fingers right off. Somehow instead of sinking to the bottom and being eaten by crabs, my fingers were turning into sea creatures. Somehow I was not drowning and could breathe underwater. Sinking, sinking, sinking—until I reached the bottom where I've lived ever since, in a world beneath the sea floor.

Here I live without fingers. Somehow I live. I'm not sure why. My hair is a tangled nest, as rank as my husband's home. Every now and then when the people who live on the ice are close to starving they send someone down to comb it. I know they don't really care about me, but it feels so good I forget for a while what my father did to me, and I open the gate at the back of my hut where a finned multitude dwells, and out they all pour again: the squid and octopi, swordfish, marlin, herring, mullet, cod, belugas, humpbacks, shrimp, lobsters, seals, and walrus. They won't know hunger for a long time, those people on the ice. Somehow I live. Someone must feed the people.

It's dark when I finish. When I stand up to leave the fish flee as one to the far side.

CHAPTER 8
THE INNOCENCE OF THE HUNTER

◎

F
OR A TIME that seemed outside of time, I lived on a small island off the Atlantic coast, Block Island, named for the Dutch explorer Adrian Block who claimed it for his country. I belonged there. The place knew me. I slept on the earth and listened to huffing deer, indignant I'd bedded down in their meadows. I stalked striped bass in seaweed-covered rocks and speared them, emerging from the sea triumphant to feed my friends at beach fires where we got drunk and sang, laughed and shrieked and loved each other just because we all lived on a small island together and saw each other every day. I was part of a tribe. I sang in a band and people called me Whitewave. In winter I walked for hours without seeing another human and was happy. I stood at the edge of fields and watched deer on the other side look back at me, both of us waiting to see who would make the first move.

It was always me. Even if it was just a twitch or the wind blowing my hair, I couldn't maintain the same stillness as the deer and they leaped back into the shadow thickets where I couldn't follow unless I crawled on my belly.

Why leave the safety and security of home for unknown dangers? I ask myself that every time I feel the magnetic pull of some new place. But I go. I follow the invisible pull, the tides in my blood tracking the moon like a buck who has walked out of the dunes to shore's edge to watch silver light break on waves. Reflection upon reflection, the mirror breaks and then shows us ourselves again with a new face. Who am I this time, in this new place without my tribe? Sunset has arrived. It's time to drive down the mountain.

When I get to the pond I stand on the rock bridge and look into the water. Some of the fish-dug depressions are now quite deep. Impressive. That's a heap of sand grains to carry in your mouth. Although it's tempting to believe some magical creatures like the menehune, who may be mythological or may be in another dimension most of us can't perceive, did it, I know in fact, the fish never stop working. I know because I've been watching them now for days. I am beginning to know this place.

I walk over to my vigil spot and sit, offer Pele her drop of gin, and look to see if the usual suspects, Big Papa and Crabby are waiting for me.

Big Papa's depression is bigger and deeper and he's got company! His amour doesn't seem fully committed to their tryst, flitting in and out of the mating bowl. Finally, he just goes for it. I watch him turn over on his side and shake his whole body over her. She doesn't stick around, darting out to join the females schooling in the center. Tiny fish, minnow-size, slip into his domain. Could be his kids. He chases them out. What harm could they possibly do you, Big Papa? They're just little squirts. Why not let them be? Are you teaching them how to catch a mate when they grow up? Are you showing them they have to fight in order to procreate? Another male swims toward him and a Darwinian face-off commences. I can hear the chest thumping, and though the water is iron-gray, I can see the feral gleam as they eye each other—kill or be killed. Will we ever escape?

As Ke'oni says, very few of us in the modern world are in imminent danger. Our ancestors when the human brain was developing were—which is why we so often feel we are about to be killed and flare up into fight or flight over modern-day threats like being stuck in traffic on the freeway or Christmas shopping at Walmart. Road rage is real. People have been trampled to death in the stampede to get the latest toys. The traumas of our ancestors live in our brains, in our livers and spleens and guts—and in our hearts. Trapped in never-ending circles of reactivity, our bodies believe we are about to be eradicated. The result? We kill ourselves. We kill each other. We kill our planet.

Crabby appears from nowhere and side winds across my field of vision, scuttling into the stone lean-to, flushing out another crab who had taken shelter there. I'm starting to feel like a prophet.

I begin to sing without words. My song takes me within, and then deeper in, a move outward. I lose myself in the water. When the song finishes I begin to speak.

THE SALMON OF KNOWLEDGE

There were rumors we began with a flood.

I bet you haven't heard that, that we Irish came to this land on the same flood that Noah saved us from with his ark, marching the animals on two-by-two until the water subsided. But despite what we like to think, we Irish aren't special. You'll find the same story in many places around the world. Cities destroyed by water. Crops wiped out, trees pulled up by the roots to float until they sank, for there was no shore to receive them. I'm sure you've all heard how Noah and his family survived, drifting on the ark until they got a sign from a white dove that land had returned, the olive branch and the rainbow, covenant of God's promise to look after us.

How did this come to be? The Irish tracing their lineage back to Noah? Well then, let me enlighten you with the story. It's a strange one that I had a hard time believing at first, too.

When Noah denied his own son Bith a place on the Ark, along with his companions Fintan MacBochra and Ladra, and his own granddaughter Cesair, the plucky lass took charge. Cesair built three more arks and promised safe transport to them all if they would acknowledge her leadership. As the waters rose, the small band gathered others left behind by Noah and made their way to Inis Fail, "The Promised Land"— Ireland.

Seven soggy years later, one ship finally reached the dry ground of Inis Fail. Only Fintan, Bith, Ladra, Cesair, and fifty women survived. On land, they divided themselves up into three groups, one man to each. Cesair, having eyes for Fintan, joined his group, but when the other two men died her beloved took on a burden he wasn't expecting. It was up to her and Fintan to populate Inis Fail.

Now this may have been a dream come true for some men, but Fintan quaked at the thought of being responsible for populating the Promised Land! Perhaps he was more of a hermit than a lover. Alas—he fled.

Brokenhearted, Cesair died soon after. All the women but warrior Banba were swept away by the Flood, leaving Fintan and Banba as the only humans left in Ireland, and that wasn't the case for long. Tossed on the wild waters, Fintan discovered his powers as a shapeshifter. To survive he became a salmon, biding his time beneath the churning surface until the waters receded.

When land appeared again, the waters shaped themselves into bodies of water. One of those limbs was the River Boyne, which Fintan discovered, and with the instinct spawned in his silvery flesh he powered his way upstream all the way to a pool ringed by nine hazel trees. Nine nuts grew on each tree that contained all the world's knowledge. One by one the nuts fell into Fintan's fish lips, traveling down his gullet to his belly. Lo and behold, they tinged his scales with all the colors of the rainbow! And that is how he became known as the Salmon of Wisdom.

I'm Finn MacCool, by the way. I haven't properly introduced myself. You may have heard of me, though my name is not as renowned as it once was when I led the Fianna, my great band of wild-living warriors—oh how we danced and fought and loved this island—but I'm getting away with myself. Tends to happen when you get older. The mind wanders to better days, or at least the glory days when we all answered the horn's call and rode out onto the mountain to hunt the deer in the deep glades where ferns released the secrets of our original ancestors into the air on gold spores. I learned some of those secrets just by galloping through them, but I was too young to know it. And the deer, what can I say? I loved her—but that is another story, which I'll tell you if you really want to hear it, if you'll come with me to another time and place where you may not hear what happened to the Salmon of Wisdom. No? You want to focus on one story? Well, that's your choice then, but I must say it's often the journey where you learn the wisdom, not the destination. Still, I aim to please so I will stay focused. It seems people in your time best understand a story that moves from A to Z without detours, so I'll make this relatable and not take you on a wild Irish ramble into the mystic.

I was born to Cumhaill and Murna, whose father Tadg (my grandfather) was so irate he killed my father and probably would have killed me if my mother had not fled. She and my aunt Bodmhall raised me on the mountainside. Bodmhall was a trainer of warriors. She actually trained many of the boys that grew up to join the Fianna, and she taught me the martial arts of Ireland. My mother was a deer woman, and from her I learned to run with the deer and to listen in all directions while standing still. Some say my mother could even become a deer, but I never saw that. To me, she was a human mother and I loved her. She called me Deimne, Little Stag, and there was nothing I loved more in the world than to curl up with her in a grove to shelter from the bright sunlight, walking out through the dusk into starlit fields of hay and wildflowers.

Sooner than my mother wanted I was faster than the deer, and soon enough my grandfather had heard of me and my mother living on the mountainside and determined to kill us. It broke my mother's heart, but she dressed me in rags and sent me off with a band of traveling bards. We sang our way across the ley lines of Ireland, in and out of many households. The bards called me Finn because I was so fair and they said I shone even when the sun didn't, which is still the case in Ireland, though who knows what will happen with global warming.

Eventually, my time with the wandering minstrels came to an end. They were talking about sailing across the great ocean in coracles and I knew I wasn't ready for that, so when they offered to escort me to a great druid master who lived in the woods near the River Boyne, I didn't say no.

Finnegas was his name, a man of deep wisdom, who wanted even more. Obsessed with what he didn't know, my new master spent hours fishing in the River Boyne, hoping to catch the famed Salmon of Knowledge, Fintan, who had eaten the nuts from the Tree of Life and knew everything there was to know in the world.

For a boy, life with Finnegas was grand. We lived in the woods with no one to tell us what to do or where to be. He taught me all the druid lore, the ballads and spells and stories, and I learned even more from the woods themselves. Often we would sit together on the banks of the Boyne reciting poetry while Finnegas dropped his line into the pool in the hopes of catching Fintan.

And then it happened—a mighty tug on the pole—and Finnegas leaping to his feet, straining with all his might to reel the catch in. With glee he hollered, "My boy, It's Fintan, himself! At last! Oh, glory!"

Beads of sweat poured down his forehead as he put his whole being into reeling that fish in, and when we could see it just beneath the water's surface—the rainbow flash—well I'll tell you, I've never seen the like before or after.

"You did it, Finnegas!" I yelped with delight, leaning toward the old man to help him haul the great Fintan onto the bank.

"Back off. I've got it," Finnegas commanded. I let him do the work himself. It was his catch and he was rightly proud of it.

I have to say I was a bit sad watching Fintan gasp on the grass next to our fire pit. Finnegas was blowing on an ember to get the flames going so he could roast and eat this wisest of beasts. He would be the greatest bard ever. What epics he would compose! The very trees shook their leaves in jubilation.

My master laid the fire, stacking kindling on the red coals and then adding larger logs. As the flames flickered and leapt into life I was watching the salmon and I saw something I've never forgotten in all my adventures with the Fianna—I met the eye of the Salmon of Knowledge just before it glazed over. Let me tell you, I'll never forget it. I was there when the rainbow left his scales, shifting right before my eyes to a dull, flat gray like a poisoned well. I watched magic leave the world.

But Finnegas was going to eat it and the magic would be restored! I was delighted for my teacher and helped him blow on the flames until the fire was roaring, rip rap. "Thank you, Finn. You're a good boy," Finnegas told me. My heart swelled with pride.

"There, just so. The coals are ready." He looked up at me. "I find myself exhausted after my exertions, though. I need to lie down and restore myself. Would you turn the spit while I rest? I'll eat the salmon when I wake up."

And that's how it happened. Finnegas propped himself against an oak. "Wake me when it's ready, boy. And don't eat even one bite!"

As he drifted off, I sat by the fire watching the fish with a falcon's intensity. I wanted it to be perfect for my master. I watched the skin crackle and fat drip into the flames with a sizzle. I tried to forget the loss of the rainbow and how the salmon's eye had met mine, but I couldn't, and maybe that's why when the fish was done and I called out to Finnegas to rouse him—"Dinner!" I couldn't forget that rainbow, and maybe that's why when I noticed a blister bubbling on the fish's roasting skin I couldn't resist popping it with my thumb, which caused my own thumb to blister. Without thinking I sucked on it, and my spontaneous act of self-soothing changed the course of history, for all the salmon's knowledge entered into me.

Finnegas saw it at once, of course. I stood before him holding up the fish for him to eat and I looked nothing like the reckless boy who'd been following him about the woods all these years. Unbelievably, considering I'd ruined his life's dream, Finnegas forgave me and told me I may as well eat the rest of the fish. He was a wise man and knew my heart was innocent.

Destiny had shown her hand to us that day in the woods and he would not resist it. I didn't either. He told me to suck my thumb whenever I needed an answer to a problem and I still do, even in my old age. He also told me that water drunk from my cupped hands could save a life. That will come into play in another story, but we're not ready yet for that one. We still have a long way to go and the direction is down. If your knees quake when you hear that, be strengthened by the knowledge I am with you.

Was it fair I received the knowledge of the world Finnegas had yearned for these many years? No, but that's not the way destiny works. I went on to become the leader of the Fianna and have had a life full of adventures. I've entered many stories and left a hundred more, and now I'm leaving this one for you to take up and tell. I encourage you to do right by my story, and to remember life isn't always fair, but justice will find you. It may not come down from a court, but life will have its way with you, and in the long run, that is justice. I know because I've lived through many other stories besides this one, where I was a young and green boy who sucked his thumb and gained the knowledge of the world that made me a great leader, but none of that protected me from a broken heart. Would you like to hear that story? Not today. I find myself tired after my exertions. I think I'll lie down and rest. Perhaps when I awake, refreshed, I'll share my stories of heartbreak. In the meantime, get some rest yourselves, my fellow travelers. Destiny always finds us, if not in this world, then the next.

According to science, suffering happens in the brain, not the heart. Turn off the nociceptors and the brain can be hacked into without the body feeling pain. Anesthesia. It's a pretty name. Like a Greek goddess or a Russian Tsarina executed in a basement.

Scientists say turn off the nociceptors in the brain and suffering will cease. But ghosts suffer. They have no bodies and they suffer. I've heard them. Remember the orca who swam for days, keeping her dead calf above the surface in the chilly Salish Sea? Suffering and pain are not the same. Suffering is not a product of fear, it's the gift of love.

Maybe ghosts have drawn me here to the Place of Refuge. If so, whose? The spirits I angered when I slept in Paka'alana all those years ago in Waipi'o? The ghosts of the Hawaiians who violated kapu and didn't make it across the water to the sanctuary?

My European ancestors who boarded ships to emigrate

may have been starving. They may have feared they'd be put to death for worshiping God as they chose. How many of them looked down and saw sharks rising up from the deep toward their tender hearts? Some of them fled, others froze. Some learned to fawn to get what they wanted. And some fought.

None of those are viable options for me anymore. I have sailed across another ocean (flown, but I'm exercising my poetic license) and descended to the bottom of a valley where I bathed in a waterfall. I journeyed back up on the sound of falling water. On that sound I make this ho'okukāla. I proclaim: *I now refresh my lineage.*

I will not be the sacrifice for my ancestors' sins or ignorance any longer. To my lineage, I say: *Thank you. I love you. I have outgrown you.* To my sins I say, in my ignorance I was innocent. I am not asking anyone's forgiveness to exist anymore. I release myself.

CHAPTER 9
THE WILDERNESS YEARS

I N 2007, after ten years of year-round living on Block Island, I boarded a plane and landed in Lima, Peru. This may not sound like that big of a deal to people who get around, but I had barely left Block Island for ten years. Going in a Cumberland Farms on a day trip to the mainland could put me in a depressed funk that would last the whole winter. I was horrified by modern life, its garish lights and mindless consumerism. Block Island was my retreat and I thought I would be there forever.

It wasn't always like that. At 18, the summer after I graduated from high school, I flew to London on a one-way ticket, ended up as an au pair in Paris for nine months, hitchhiked from Barcelona to Brindisi, and spent a truly bacchanalian month in the Greek isles before AIDS when everybody was on the pill. I returned to the United States and went to college in Washington, DC, where I lived into the early 90s, striding drunken miles home across the city through the "bad" neighborhoods.

I probably should have been afraid. DC was the murder capital of the US in those days, but I wasn't. I remember watching my shadow stride down the sidewalk, backlit by streetlights, and thinking *nobody is going to fuck with me*. A guy even told me that once. "If I was going to jump someone on the street it wouldn't be you." Back then, I took things like that as a compliment.

In reality, I was just lucky. I made it unscathed despite making many foolish and horrendous choices. I may have looked confident, but inside me was a jungle orchid dropped in a desert with no idea how it had arrived in a place without water. Driven to flower by the green pulse within me I begged for water to stay alive and took whatever drops the sky deigned to grant me. My middle initial "D" didn't stand for Denise, but for depression, so familiar it was part of my name.

I was so unable to conceive a future I didn't even know I was missing one. My days consisted of working in a bookstore and getting drunk with my friends at night. I dreamed of the next party where I'd meet the dream lover who would adore me forever and then I'd get a book deal and live happily ever after. No wonder I was depressed.

And then a small box turtle poked its head out of a pond ringed by cattails on an island 13 miles out to sea. The turtle looked up at the low-lying clouds, heavy with rain, and blinked. The blink happened at turtle speed, what we'd call slow motion. It drew its lids down over its eyes, paused and rested for a moment in darkness, and then lifted them just as slowly. There was no rush, no eagerness, no expectation. Nothing looked different—the clouds were still there, low-lying and ready to release their life-giving rain, but the whole sky was different. Though I didn't know it, that turtle was my anchor—a piece of my soul outside my skin's limits—and it was calling me.

I didn't hear it. I was much too hungover. But my Dad came to my rescue, driving down from Connecticut to DC and swooping me and my cat Bea up and transporting us to that island where the turtle had blinked, where my family had owned a summer cottage near that cattail ringed pond, and where my mother once led my brother and me down to its edge to release a box turtle that had wandered out of the water and onto our lawn.

Shaking the city off like a tranquilized she-wolf, I landed on Block Island full of bravado and slipped into the summer worker scene serving tourists drinks and coffee. I was hot, smart, and a poet. I could party. Most people liked me. There were ghosts following me, but I managed to push them away. Sometimes I even ran from them, jogging home from the bars intoxicated by the aroma of blackberry blossoms and beach roses rising up out of the marsh below me while the moon smiled down on me, licking his lips at the coming feast. The moon isn't just a harsh mistress, he's also a husband, one you don't usually know you've married until you are called to find your own light.

The winter I turned 30, I decided to stay put. My bags were packed and I told my ride to the ferry I wasn't going.

I needed to let winter have its way with me. On a 9.75 square mile-thirteen miles out to sea island with a population of 900, an island cruise—an entire loop around the island—took 15 minutes. Everyone knew everyone and if they didn't they thought they did, and felt free to make up a story about your life for their own entertainment. Some of my friends chafed at the lack of anonymity, but I never minded. I felt safe on Block Island. Year after year I walked, rode my bike, partied in the summer, wrote in the winter, fell in and out of love, visited friends and relatives in the graveyard, and made friends I will have to my dying day. Like I said, I thought I would never leave.

But the first few winters were brutal. I lived alone in the attic apartment of a hundred year old inn that was closed for the season. The inn owners were my employers, I worked for them running the inn in the busy season, but they were more like fairy godparents, putting up with all sorts of shenanigans from us chambermaids. In summer, I lived out back in a barn that was considered prime housing on Block Island where most of us workers got booted from our winter housing in actual homes to dwell in shacks, boats, basements and barns so our winter quarters could be rented out for thousands a week. In winter, walking past the empty rooms to get to my door, the ghosts of a hundred years of guests watched me. Most days my only social interaction was walking downhill to the post office at 4:30 in the dark to ask for my mail at the counter. When I got a PO Box I didn't even have this small pleasure. There was one bar. One grocery store. The library, the only indoor refuge. The winter it closed they moved some books into the produce bin at the grocery store. This was before the internet, before Amazon could drop off anything you wanted at your doorstep. Browsing those produce bins for something to read was a ritual that kept me from completely disintegrating, the books themselves kept me stitched together enough to survive the depression by weaving me into someone else's dreams.

I want to say it was unbearable, but it wasn't. I survived. My body kept on living without me doing a thing besides feeding and watering, even though I kept doing my best to abandon it by getting stupid drunk and continuing with my reckless ways.

One late October afternoon, heading toward the West Side, driving too fast past the graveyard, something burst in my brain, an aneurysm of pain. The thought *I just want this to be over* pulsed so bright, for a moment, it took away my vision. Driving blind, I sent a wordless prayer out to the nothing I believed in. *Take me away from here. Relieve me of this body.*

Someone heard me. We had been moving toward each other before we were born. In the dark, the place where we go to forget the light, we had once known each other. In the dark, the place of re-membering, we curled around each other like twins in a womb, unaware we'd ever be parted. We slid from the dark when it was time, spiraled back into the light that blinded, forgot each other.

Is that why life was so painful? We'd lost track of each other? My wild twin, my soul's mate who had shared that primal darkness with me. My Jeep was shooting down the road now, wheels spinning so fast there was no way I could stop—collision was the only way. *Please, get me out of here. I just want this to be over.*

Out of the dusk, not quite night or day, a deer leaped in front of my Jeep Cherokee and surged uphill into the graveyard. I missed it by a hair's width through no action of my own. I hadn't even had time to shift my foot to the brake. In the rearview mirror I saw its twin—another deer followed her sister up into the graves. If I had struck them, we might have all died, but they passed around me like a river. My hands were still on the wheel.

You might think I just got lucky, but when I pulled into my driveway with my hands still shaking on the steering wheel, I knew it wasn't luck, but grace that lifted my Jeep in its waters for a few seconds, spun me around and set me back down on Earth with the memory I would track down for the next seven years. I had two wild sisters. Some might think I had saved them by not hitting them, some might think they had saved me, but nobody saved anyone. We remembered each other, how three of us were one in the dark without longing for the light, enveloped in a great heartbeat. I began the long, slow climb out of the Underworld on my human feet.

I wish I could give you a clear timeline of the journey, but it didn't happen that way. I walked alone in virgin snow after storms that shook the house until I found the trees where the cardinals hid from the wind. I followed deer tracks down dune paths that stopped at the edge of the ocean and swam in all seasons, even winter when the shock of cold rattled my bones against each other loud enough for me to realize they were still holding me up. Year after year, from the kitchen table where I wrote, I watched a harrier return to hunt in the thicket. It took me a couple of years to realize it was *the same harrier*. Without making a conscious vow, I realized I was in a committed relationship. I undertook a serious study of the craft of poetry—where to break the line, how to open a heart.

Eleven winters in, the snowy owl I'd been hoping to see for years showed up on my doorstep. Facing the field in front of the house, its neck pivoted completely around on the axis of its white-feathered body. Yellow eyes bored through my pretenses and excuses. *Claim your life,* they seemed to say. When it turned its head to face away from me, I knew I was free. Block Island, known by its original inhabitants as Manisses, Island of the Little God, had released me.

Am I still in the same story? That's the first thing I think when I come out of my reverie. Yes, I am still here, inside the park gates just on the other side of the Great Wall in the Pu'uhonu-anua o Hōnaunau, the Place of Refuge. Big Papa and Crabby are here, though I can't see them. The birds—'ulili and auku'u—are here. One stalking the shadows, another showing me I'm right on course, dashing through the air on a sweet cry that expresses the pure love of flying, even though it knows one day the ground will claim its feathers. The stones here are black and sharp, closer to fire than the smooth quartz pebbles of home that crack and explode in the fire. I know this from times building a sweat lodge on Block Island, where it was a challenge to find stones that could sustain the heat without shattering. The heat used to terrify me. The darkness even more. Now I have come to this place where the land is much closer to fire. It lets me sit upon it without being burned, though sometimes when I'm not careful it trips me up and I end up with a gash on my leg I just might need. I've seen a lot of stupid haoles with staph infections. Antibiotics can't cure everything anymore. We are in times whose rules we don't know yet. It's time to begin asking questions that acknowledge we are in unknown territory, instead of puffing out our chests and pretending we have an answer to everything, thinking this gives us the right to take what we want.

Imagine if every potential colonizer asked, *Water, what do you want? Little fish and crabs and the Queen of the Pond, you silver goddess, what do you want?* What would our planet look like if every person who'd ever left their home with the intent to conquer, possess or impose their beliefs on another place asked these questions, listened, and respected these non-human voices?

There is no time for subservience. Leave off asking for forgiveness for being an ignorant and sloppy human and get on with it. The water is waiting. The ancestors who crossed oceans in thin-hulled ships that could have been punctured at any moment, who respected fire because it could burn the ship down and who watched candles respond to their anxious breathing—would they make it across—they made it. We are the results. I am the result. I have crossed over. I have wings. I can fly. I have a boat. I can carry two: my love and I. *I am my love.* The ancestors, the spirits of this place, listen to my stuttering heart and call out, *when will you finally sing?*

THE MOON MAN

There was a man who lived in a tent in the far north with his only daughter. She was a lively girl with the bright eyes of a crow and cheeks red as tundra berries. They were reindeer herders, following their beasts around the tundra as the seasons changed.

The girl's special companion was a reindeer ox. She drove that ox everywhere, even into the deepest snows that fell upon the tundra in the heart of winter. Her trust in him was absolute. She would have followed him anywhere.

One day on one of their adventures, the girl looked up and saw a marvelous sight in the sky—a Moon Man flying through the air on a sled pulled by reindeer.

"Hide!" her reindeer told her as soon as he saw the sled. Quickly, he dug a hole in the snow for her with his hooves and the girl jumped in. The reindeer covered her and no part of her could be seen above the earth.

Just as the reindeer pushed the last scoop of snow over her, the Moon Man touched down. "I saw you, Chukchi Girl!" he shouted. "Where are you? I'm here to carry you off to the sky!" He began to hunt, but couldn't find her. Finally, he jumped back in the sled and the reindeer carried him back to the sky.

The girl burrowed out from under the safety of her snow mound, climbed on her reindeer's back, and journeyed home.

No one was there. Her father was gone.

Looking down from the sky, the Moon Man caught his second glimpse of her and charged back down to earth on his sled.

"Hide!" said the reindeer ox.

"Where can I hide?" the girl replied, frantic.

"I know," the ox said, "I'll turn you into a tent pole, or a hair on the skin of the tent. Wait—I know where to hide you. I'll turn you into a lamp. The Moon Man will be blinded by his own light and never find you."

And so the reindeer turned her into a lamp, not realizing the light from it would be so bright the whole tent would be illuminated, once again catching the eye of the Moon Man.

Back he came in a rush, huffing and puffing. He tore the tent apart, searched every box, shook out the skins that kept the girl and her father warm. He didn't find her.

The reindeer was right. Because the Moon Man was bright, he couldn't see the lamp. The girl was safe. The Moon Man went back to the sky.

Well, it seemed at this point the girl might have been enjoying this game of hide-and-seek, for as soon as the Moon Man left, the girl, back in her human form, ran out of the tent and yelled up at him, "Moon Man! Here I am!" Shaking his antlers, the ox turned her back into a lamp as the Moon Man, slowly this time, began another descent to earth.

"Where are you, Chukchi Girl? You will be mine! I will carry you up to the sky!" The Moon Man chanted as he searched. Once again he failed and headed back to the sky.

Once again, as soon as she was back in human form, the girl taunted him. "Here I am!"

No slow and measured descent this time. The Moon Man was angry. He rushed back and tore into the tent. "Where are you, Chukchi Girl? You will be mine! I will carry you up to the sky!" This time he searched under every stone, twig and leaf— and still didn't find her.

Back and forth, from sky to earth, the Moon Man traveled all night long. He was obsessed with finding the girl. Eventually, his rage wore him out. Weakened, now he stuttered through the sky. The girl saw her chance.

"Turn me back into a human," she whispered to her reindeer ox. As soon as he did she leaped onto the Moon Man's back and lassoed him, pulling the rope tight. "I don't want to live in the sky!"

"Untie me," the Moon Man pleaded, "Or I'll die."

"But you want to kill me."

"Please. I'm so cold. Let me go into the tent to warm up. I need shelter."

For a moment, the girl felt sorry for him. She knew what it was like to be cold, the relief of burrowing under furs after a long journey on the snow-covered tundra.

"All right," she began, but wait! He must be trying to trick her. "How could you be cold?" she asked the Moon Man. "You live in the sky. What possible need could you have for my skins?"

The Moon Man, realizing she was onto him, decided to strike a bargain. "Please set me free, Chukchi Girl. I'll return to the sky and give you a gift. I will light up the sky and measure time for you."

Seemed like a fair negotiation. Chukchi Girl agreed, though she was on guard. He had tricked her before. How could she trust him?

But this time the Moon Man wasn't trying to trick her. Like her, he just wanted to live. To prove himself, he began to recite the thirteen names for the moon as it passed through its cycles, making poetry out of time.

> Moon of Icicle Swords
> Goose Down Moon
> Moon of Shedding Antlers
> Moon of the Singing Tree Frogs
> Snapping Turtle Moon
> Moon of the Spotted Fawns
> The Long Sun Moon
> Moon of Lengthening Shadows
> Cornucopia Moon
> Falling Leaf Moon
> Moon of the Stags' Rut
> Rattling Serpent Moon
> Howling Wolf Moon

The girl was enchanted by his litany, the beautiful turn of his words, but she had earned her wisdom.

"If I set you free won't you come back?" He had, after all, done just that three times.

"No, Chukchi Girl, you are too clever for me. I'll keep my end of the bargain."

So the Chukchi Girl untied the rope and set the Moon Man free. He kept his word and flew back to the sky on his sled, and this time he stayed there. He lit the sky up himself and showed them how to measure time by waxing and waning.

Did the Moon Man mind being stuck in the sky? Did he dream of the Chukchi Girl down below and wish he could carry her up to be his wife? I don't know, the story tells us he wasn't lonely anymore. The earthlings were his company and their gaze upon his radiance was the companionship he needed. For them, he waxed and waned, showing them faces on his surface like a moving picture in an old dancehall. He had a purpose, the Moon Man. Sometimes that's all it takes.

CHAPTER 10
A TRICKSTER'S LOVE

◉

C LOUDS TUMBLE down the slopes of Mauna Loa and strike the rocks rimming the ponds like Zeus's thunderbolts. The relief of violence. In less than a minute I am pummeled, soaked to the bone, and the stack of paper I clutch dissolved into pulp. The papers contain today's story—a big one I didn't feel I could tell on my own. Now I have no choice. The ponds are dancing like pointillist paintings. When I look at them they disappear and appear before my eyes. With blue lips, I stand before them and begin the story:

THE DESCENT OF INANNA

Was I prepared when I heard the call of the Great Below? No. No one is. Not even a goddess like me. I abandoned my temples. I gathered together the seven visible powers of my divinity. I knew I would need them to face the dangers of the Underworld. I knew there was no guarantee I'd make it back again to this world I loved so—the world of honey wine and my sweet shepherd Dumuzi, a world of flute song and feathered fingertips brushing over my oiled body, the smell of frankincense and jasmine, of flower baths and long, deep kisses that melted me in places that weren't even frozen. Oh, how I loved this world—my sweet shepherd, the adoration in the temples. It would be more than hard to leave, but I had heard my sister Ereshkigal's call.

I placed the shugurra on my head, the crown of the steppe where the horses were wild and arranged my mane of raven-black hair artfully across my forehead. I was both coy and commanding.

Next, I roped a double-strand of lapis beads around my neck, bright blue beads draping over my breasts. The chill of the stone raised my nipples and I shivered, wondering if I'd ever again feel the nip of my husband's teeth.

I wrapped the royal robe around my body and daubed my eyes with the ointment so aptly named, "Let Him Come, Let Him Come!" I bound the breastplate called, "Come, Man, Come!" to my chest. I was ready to face whatever Ereshkigal could throw at me.

When I'd slipped the gold ring over my finger and took the lapis measuring rod and line in hand, I was ready, except for one last thing. I turned to my faithful servant Ninshubur.

"Ninshubur, my faithful servant, I am bound for the Underworld. This may be the last time you'll see me. My sister is wailing in the deep and I must go to her."

"I know, I know, I hear you. Let her be. What has she ever done for me? But for some reason I can't explain, I know I just have to go down. Something beyond me requires it. I have to go."

Ninshubur regarded me in silence. She would do anything for me. I knew that.

"Before I go, I'll ask one last thing of you, dear servant. If in three days I don't return, arrange a lament for me by the ruins and beat a drum for me in the assembly places. Circle the gods' houses. Tear at your eyes and mouth and thighs. Dress yourself in a single garment like a beggar. Go to Nippur, to the temple of Enlil, Lord of the Wind, and beseech him not to let his daughter be put to death in the Underworld. Beseech him not to let me, his bright silver, grow dull; me, his precious lapis be covered with dust and broken into stone, his fragrant box-wood cut and burned. Tell him, that I who am all this beauty, am in the Underworld and he must save me."

"If Enlil refuses, go to Ur, to the temple of Nanna. Weep before Father Nanna, god of the moon. If Nanna will not help you, Go to Eridu, to the temple of Enki. Weep before Father Enki. Father Enki, god of wisdom, god of water, god of mischief, will know what to do. He knows the secret of the food and water of life. He won't let me die."

I left Ninshubur and continued on. Down, down, down I walked until I arrived at the outer gates of the Underworld. I knocked and cried out in a bold voice, "Gatekeeper, open the door!"

It took more than a bold knock to get Neti to open the gate. "Who are you?" he demanded.

"I am Inanna, Queen of Heaven," I thundered. "On my way to the East. Open the gate."

Even though I knew he believed me, it wasn't his job to make getting through the gate easy. "If you are truly Inanna, Queen of Heaven, on your way to the East," he countered, "why has your heart led you on the road from which no traveler returns?"

I didn't cajole or pander to him. I gave him the simple truth. I was a Queen, take it or leave it. "I journey on the road from which no traveler returns to answer the cries of my older sister, Ereshkigal, Queen of the Underworld. Her husband, Gugalan-na, the Bull of Heaven, has died. I have come to witness the funeral rites."

"Well, then," Neti spoke, as if this was just an ordinary day,

"Stay here. I will speak to my queen. I will relay your message." He turned from me and retreated from the outer gate, disappearing into the deep interior where my sister awaited me. She knew I was coming. I could hear it in her wailing. Our showdown had been fated since the moment the world had been made.

Being a goddess and a queen I had superpowers. I could hear Neti clearly when he came before my sister's throne. "My Queen, a maid tall as heaven, wide as earth, strong as the foundation of a city wall waits outside the palace gates. She says she is your sister. She has gathered the seven sacred objects. She is wearing the shugurra on her brow, her dark hair is carefully arranged, the lapis beads are around her throat and the double strand of beads adorn her breastbone. She is wrapped in the royal robe and her eyes are wide with the ointment 'Let Him Come, Let Him Come.' Her chest bears the breastplate, 'Come, Man, Come!' The gold ring is on her finger. She carries the lapis measuring rod and line in her hand. She says she is here to witness your husband's funeral rites. She is asking to see you. Should I let her enter?"

Ereshkigal heard all this. Her husband Gugallana, the Bull of Heaven, was dead at the hands of Enki and Gilgamesh. I had played a part in his death, but we both knew I was just following the course of our shared fate. And now here I was, right on time, playing my part, saying I wanted to witness the funeral rites. Even though she knew I would come, I could understand why she might not be pleased to see me. I had played a part in the death of her husband.

"Neti, my gatekeeper," Ereshkigal spoke. "This is what you shall do: Bolt the seven gates of the Underworld, then, open them one by one—just a crack. Let Inanna enter. As she enters, remove her royal garments. Let the Queen of Heaven enter bowed low before me."

Neti returned to me, bolting the gates behind him. He

opened the outer gate, just enough for me to slip through. "Enter," he proclaimed.

When I entered, he motioned I should remove the shugurra from her head. "What's this?" I demanded. "Remove my crown?"

"Hush, Inanna," Neti told me. "The ways of the Underworld are perfect and may not be questioned."

I could see I had no choice. I didn't need a crown to know I was a queen. I removed the shugurra, and with my hair tumbling in disarray to my shoulders, stepped fully into the Underworld and began walking to the second gate.

Once again, Neti opened the gate just a crack. This time he took my lapis beads. "What is this?" I asked once again.

The reply was the same, "Hush, Inanna. The ways of the Underworld are perfect and may not be questioned." I loved those beads, but the earth's veins were rich with lapis. I would always have beads. I was the Queen of Heaven.

At the third gate, Neti removed the double strand of lapis that adorned my breast, the ones that peaked my nipples and made my inner thighs tremble when I thought of Dumuzi's lips on my honey pot. "What is this?" I was a little more shaken this time. If Neti noticed, he didn't show it, answering in the same flat voice. "Hush, Inanna. The ways of the Underworld are perfect and may not be questioned."

When Neti opened the fourth gate to let me squeeze through, he took my breastplate. "Let Him Come, Let Him Come!" was removed. Before I could even ask, Neti answered: "Hush, Inanna, the ways of the Underworld are perfect and may not be questioned." So used to being in control, I was taken aback that he hadn't even waited for me to speak, but I knew if I wanted to reach my sister I had to obey him.

At the fifth gate, I offered my hand before he asked so he could remove the gold ring. Neti smiled like a dragon hoarding a treasure, hissing the answer to the question I mouthed without sound as if he'd stolen my voice, "What is this?"

"Hush, Inanna, the ways of the Underworld are perfect and may not be questioned."

When I slipped through the cracked sixth gate, he took the lapis measuring rod and line from my hand.

I still had some pride. "What is this?"

Neti's reply didn't vary: "Hush, Inanna, the ways of the Underworld are perfect and may not be questioned."

Things were different at the seventh gate. Stripped of all signs of royalty and divinity, Neti told me now to remove my royal robe. "You will walk into the Underworld naked."

"What is this?"

"Hush, Inanna, the ways of the underworld are perfect and may not be questioned."

I entered my sister's throne room naked. She rose and looked down on me. Now would be the moment we'd be reunited, all forgiven, grudges dropped, my sister, my Dark Queen! I took a step toward her.

Before my foot could touch the ground the Annuna, Ereshhkigal's judges, swarmed me, striking me dead with one blow. No chance to defend myself. No opportunity to explain. Already naked, I was now dead meat hanging upside down from a hook on the wall.

For three days and nights, I hung there. The memory still makes me shudder. I wish that I had no memory of that time, of how after three days my grief-stricken servant Ninshubur set up a lament for me by the ruins and in the assembly places, just like she'd promised. She beat the drum for me and circled the gods' houses. She tore at her eyes like I'd told her, and her mouth; she tore at her thighs. It was too awful to describe. How she bled and wailed while the dogs circled, expecting her to drop at any moment.

Dressed in a single garment like a beggar she did as I

instructed, setting out for the temple of Enlil. When she entered the shrine she called out: "Father Enlil, god of wind, don't let your daughter be put to death in the Underworld!"

"Don't let your bright silver be covered with dust, your lapis broken into stone for the stoneworker, your boxwood cut for the woodworker. Don't let the holy priestess of Heaven die in the Underworld!"

Angry Enlil, god of wind, answered, "Inanna, my daughter craved the Great Above. Why wasn't it enough? She had to crave the Great Below. Anyone who receives the regalia of the Underworld does not return." He wouldn't help, the bastard.

Faithful Ninshubur didn't give up. I knew I could trust her. She set off for Ur and the temple of the moon god, Nanna. When she entered the holy shrine she cried out. "Father Nanna, don't let your daughter be put to death in the underworld! Don't let your bright silver be covered with dust, your precious lapis broken into stone for the stoneworker. Don't let your fragrant boxwood be cut into wood for the woodworker. Don't let the holy priestess of heaven be put to death in the Underworld!"

Father Nanna's answer was no different from Enlil's. "My daughter craved the Great Above. And then she craved the Great Below. She who receives the *me* of the underworld does not return. She who goes to the Dark City stays there." Father Nanna wouldn't help either.

Ninshubur journeyed on to our last hope, the temple of Eridu where Enki, god of water, dwelt. When she entered the holy shrine she cried out. "Father Enki, don't let your daughter be put to death in the Underworld! Don't let your bright silver be covered with dust, your precious lapis broken into stone for the stoneworker. Don't let your fragrant boxwood be cut into wood for the woodworker. Don't let the holy priestess of heaven be put to death in the Underworld!"

"What's happened?" Enki asked. My corpse sighed in relief. "What's my daughter done? My dear Inanna, Holy Priestess of

Heaven! Of course I'll help!"

He listened to Ninshubur, and when she was done, Enki, who was also the god of mischief, removed dirt from under his fingernail and molded the dirt into a kurgarra, a creature neither male nor female. From the dirt under his other fingernail, he shaped a galatur.

"Listen up you androgynous mischievous imps," he addressed his creations. "You, kurgarra, take the food of life. Galatur, you carry the water of life. When you get to the Underworld gates turn yourselves into flies and buzz on through. Keep going till you get to the throne room."

"Ereshkigal is about to give birth to her dead husband's child. She will be moaning. You will find her naked, bare-breasted, her hair swirling around her head like leeks. Don't be afraid. Hold yourself together and transform back into your imp shape. She will be in too much pain to wonder how you got there. When she starts to cry out, 'Oh! Oh! My inside!' you cry out also, 'Oh! Oh! My inside!' Echo whatever she says. She will be pleased and offer you a gift. Refuse everything she offers. Ask for only one thing: the corpse hanging on a meathook from the wall."

The kurgarra and the galatur set out for the Underworld. They slipped through the cracks in the gates as flies and flew to Ereshkigal's throne room. It was just as Enki said. No linen was covering her. Her breasts were uncovered. She was naked and hair swirled around her head like leeks. She was moaning. *Oh! Oh!* They moaned back. She was groaning. *Oh! Oh!* They groaned back. She moaned and groaned about her back and her belly, her heart, and her liver. It was piteous to hear. No matter how much she moaned and groaned, they didn't desert her. They groaned back. They moaned back.

"Who are you, moaning and sighing with me?" she finally asked. "If you are gods, I will bless you. If you are mortals, I'll give you a gift—endless water, the river in its fullness."

The kurgarra and galatur remembered what Enki had told them. "We don't want the gift of endless water, the river in its fullness," they told her.

Ereshkigal insisted. "I will give you fields of grain for harvest."

Not even tempted, the kugarra and galatur remained firm. "We don't want your fields of grain."

"Well, then," Ereshkigal snapped, "What *do* you want?" Seriously. She was a Queen and they were two imps with mud on their faces.

Their answer was not what she expected: "We only want that corpse hanging on the meathook."

"The corpse belongs to Inanna," Ereshkigal told them.

"Whether it belongs to our queen or our king, That is our wish."

My sister gave them my corpse. Before she knew what was happening the imps had sprinkled the food and water of life on my dead flesh. That was all it took to bring me back to life. Easy, right? I rose again. But the story isn't over...

Just as I was about to make my dignified ascent to be reunited with my faithful Ninshubur, my sons, and my lusty husband Dumuzi, I was seized. I knew better than to struggle."No one ascends from the Underworld unmarked," Neti the Gatekeeper had told me.

Someone was going to have to take my place.

I rose, not triumphant as I'd expected, but with the galla clinging to my side. Those demons who didn't eat or drink, who didn't accept offerings or drink libations or accept gifts, who didn't even enjoy lovemaking and had no sweet children to kiss, would trail me or take me back down. Who would take my place in the Underworld?

Outside the palace gates, Ninshubur waited in a torn and

dirty dress. When she saw me emerge surrounded by the galla she threw herself at my feet in the dust. The galla said, "Walk on, Inanna. We shall take Ninshubur in your place."

"No!" I cried. "Not Ninshubur. She didn't forget me. Ninshubur is the one who set up a lament for me at the ruins and beat the drum for me at the assembly places. She is the one who circled the gods' houses. Look at her dressed like a beggar!"

"Ninshubur tore at her own eyes and mouth and thighs. She did everything I asked—set off alone to the temple of Enlil at Nippur to ask for help. When Enlil refused, she journeyed to Ur and beseeched Nanna. When Nanna said no, she kept on going to Eridu. She never gave up. She found Enki, who sent the kurgarra and galatur to revive me. She saved my life. I will never give Ninshubur to you. You may not take her."

The galla didn't argue. "Walk on," was all they said. "We will go with you to Umma."

In Umma at the holy shrine, they found Shara, my son, dressed in dirty sackcloth. When he saw me with the galla clinging to me he threw himself at my feet, gagging on the dust. The galla said, "Walk on to your city, Inanna. We will take Shara in your place."

"No! Not Shara! Not my son who sings hymns to me. Who cuts and smoothes my hair. I will never give him to you!"

Again, they didn't protest. "Walk on," the bloodless galla said. "We will journey with you to Badtibira."

I knew they were playing the long game, that there was no denying them, but I didn't know what else to do. I walked on as they told me, dreading the moment I knew would come, though not knowing who I could possibly sacrifice.

When we got to the holy shrine at Badtibira we found Lulal, my other son, mourning in dirty sackcloth. He, too, threw himself at my feet when he saw the galla clinging to my robe.

"Inanna, walk on," the galla repeated. "We will take Lulal in your place."

Inanna cried out, "No! Not my son Lulal. He is a great leader, my right arm. My left arm! I will never give him up." Relentless, patient, the galla said to me, "Walk on to your city, Inanna. We will go with you to the big apple tree in Uruk."

In Uruk, by the big apple tree, we found Dumuzi, my sweet husband, not in mourning, not in sackcloth with torn hair and thighs, but dressed in shining garments, reveling in the royalty he gained by marrying me. The galla stayed silent. Nobody spoke.

Nobody needed to. Dumuzi knew the moment he saw my eyes. Resistance was futile. Before he could move, the galla seized him, knocking over his seven churns so that his cream poured onto the ground. They broke his reed pipe. Dumuzi would take my place in the Underworld.

Dumuzi blubbered of course. He was a mama's boy and I had coddled him, too. He raised his hands to Utu, the God of Justice, and begged."Utu! I'm your brother-in-law. Your sister's husband. This is just a bit of temporary insanity. I know you remember the truth of who I am. I brought cream to your mother's house and milk to Ningal. I carried food to the holy shrine and wedding gifts to Uruk. I am the one who danced on the holy knees of Inanna! I know you are just and merciful. Change me into a snake so that I can escape from these demons! Don't let them hold me!"

Utu, unlike me, was merciful. He accepted Dumuzi's crocodile tears. He changed him into a snake and my pan-piping, creamy-hipped husband escaped. The demons could not hold him.

By the time I'm done, the rain has abated, a steady pummeling beat against skin and rock swallows my words as if one of the world's greatest epics meant nothing. The pond is burnished gold and the reflection of the smaller palm that still has fronds almost touches my feet at the water's edge. The fish remain quiet, undisturbed in their dreaming.

So much rain fell during my oration, the bridge between the two ponds breached and they are now flowing into each other. I stand up and watch the water flow back and forth. It occurs to me they are like the two hemispheres of the brain; the left, larger pond, reflecting the half we value—the rational and analytical; the smaller right pond, that which we denigrate: intuition and imagination. The bridge I've been on all this time is the corpus callosum that divides the hemispheres.

Until today, the barrier of the callosum has been absolute, right and left cut off from each other, the right pond much smaller. What will happen now that the water is flowing back and forth?

There is more to this story, but for today it's complete. On the drive uphill I see a spotlight. Blinded, I can't tell what's happening until I'm right on it. Young people are standing transfixed in its beam, focused on the abyss beyond the light's circumference. I remember: it's a crash sight. Right here last week a girl died when the car she was in hit the rail and catapulted into the ravine below. People have made a shrine of it, bringing flowers and stuffed animals. The girl was a local, driving with two local boys—drunk I heard. The two boys lived. What made them swerve?

Tonight the flowers are lit up, the tattered teddy bears, the gash in the metal. I know in my bones when I drive past, the light was left there by the dead girl's mother. Somewhere on this mountain, a mother is mourning. *Why her? Why my daughter?* I hear the mother asking from somewhere on the quivering flank of Mauna Loa. They say she will erupt again soon. She's been dormant for too long. Fire will flow down this road someday and consume the girl's shrine and no one will be able to find the spot where her life was sacrificed.

In pua'aehuehu, grief is correlated with completion and triumph. Grief occurs when something has reached totality and we, who have not, have to let it go. We are not good at grief. We lose ourselves in loss and hardly ever reach the triumph of completion. Creating from a hollow center, following the cries of the lost, we recreate loss in a repeating loop that keeps us chained to despair and resentment.

The girl in the car that burst into flames will not come back from the Underworld. She was a human girl, not a goddess. She is complete. I pray her mother and all who loved her can mourn her to completion, that grief is fulfilled. I pray I can release my own losses and the losses of my ancestors who were never mourned properly.

Mauna Loa, Long Mountain, do you remember your source, the days when you were fire itself seeping through a crack, or even before that when you were a cloud of gas loosely swirling around an axis that wasn't yet quite solid? Are you aware of gravity pressing down on you?

Bless those who weep on your flanks, these dry foothills where the bleating goats roam. One day, despite anything we want, you will release your lava and fire will flow down the mountain. May those who survive, stand at the edge and watch land give birth to itself.

CHAPTER 11
CHOSEN BY THE LION

T HE NEXT DAY I return and consider the smaller pond in terms of yesterday's revelation that the ponds mirror the human brain. What could it mean that the left pond, domain of logic and straight-line thinking, is so much larger than the one on the right? The cloudy water in the smaller, right-pond signifies, for me, our obscured collective imagination. We are beginning to see, with some clarity, what damage we have done to Earth, but our imagination is so crippled we don't even believe it anymore. We don't believe we can save ourselves.

I'm no exception. From the beginning, I haven't been drawn to the pond on the right. I headed straight for the larger, clear pond on the first day of the ceremony. The right-hand pond is small and murky, and the few fish I glimpse, sluggish. No crabs, no enticing ripples on the surface that could be messages from spirits. Today I will give it some attention. I sit down, squint into the sun, tuck knees to my chest. My toes dangle just above the water. Now that I'm here, I see another reason I prefer the left. Facing right, I'm also facing the path that channels tourists through the park.

A group passes by. I avoid eye contact, keep my focus on the water, the shifts of light and wind that could predict the future or pull me into the past where I could have died in the cabin built next to the taro patch where heart-shaped leaves bobbed above the muddy water, the only witness to my screams. I want to think nobody came to save me because the sound of the waterfall drowned them, but when our nearest neighbor bellowed at dusk like Tarzan I heard him just fine. I swear if the wind was right I could even hear him crack open a beer can. There were no phones in the valley back then to call the police, but even if there were I don't think anyone would have called. Waipi'o was not that kind of place. People disappeared there. It was accepted.

"Nobody gets out of the Underworld unmarked," the galla said.

How could I end up in this situation? You may be wondering. All I can say is it felt like I was caught by a river and the banks were too high for me to climb out. I forgot everything but keeping my head above the water after my boyfriend flipped a switch in my mind, twisting my nipple while walking down a dirt road in broad daylight until it bruised, branding my neck with hickies so everyone knew he owned me. I would be nothing in Waipi'o without him, he told me. I believed him and retreated so deep inside myself, I was a walking, talking robot pretending everything was OK, not saying a word when his family came down on weekends, lying to his aunty who asked me if he hit me. "He throw one mango at you?" She demanded, pointing at an orange splat on the cabin porch just at head level.

"No," I lied without hesitation. I had the chance to be saved and didn't take it. That is the worst shame.

PSYCHE AND EROS

It was not my fault I was born so beautiful that the birds crashed into buildings to get a glimpse of me, that the river stopped flowing in the hopes I would touch it before it carried on to the sea. Not my fault at all. I would have changed places with my older sisters in a minute, the two of them already married, while I lingered on the shelf because my beauty was so intimidating no one would even speak to me. It was not my fault they whispered, "Psyche is more beautiful than Aphrodite," when I passed through the village. I wanted to turn and tell them to be silent, terrified Aphrodite would hear them and curse me, but I knew that would make me even more lonely.

Aphrodite heard their talk, of course. She was the Goddess of Love. Her ears were always attuned to praise. Distance was not an obstacle. She was livid. She ordered her son Eros, God of Desire, to come down from Olympus and punish me. He was to make me fall in love with the most hideous creature anyone could imagine. My beauty would be devoured by a monster.

My poor father, at his wit's end at not being able to marry me off, consulted Apollo's oracle who told him the gods were angry with me. My destiny was to marry a hideous, flying snake. The only way to appease them was to tie me to a mountain crag and let the winged serpent take me.

I'd like to tell you that my father refused, but he dressed me in a wedding gown and sent me up the mountain. Tied to the crag, I resigned myself to my fate. At least I would no longer be lonely. I didn't know it at the time, but Eros was watching me. Instead of making me fall in love with the monster, he fell madly in love with me. He commanded the West Wind, Zephyr, to waft me off the mountaintop. I landed in a magnificent palace with gold walls and marble floors. I was bedecked with jewels, bathed in sweet-scented water, massaged with precious oils, and led to a bed chamber where I was told their master, my new husband, would soon come to visit me.

He touched me in the dark, even though I begged for the light. Not because I was terrified, but because I longed to see his beauty, the magnificent stranger who introduced my body to pleasure in shudders and shouts that went on all through the night. I was consumed with desire for him. It was like my body knew before I did the delights that awaited me, like we'd been together a thousand lifetimes and only my mind had forgotten.

On and on it went, the nights of consuming passion where we feasted on each other. He always left before dawn and except for the servants, I saw no one. I was still lonely. I even missed my sisters who were never really that nice to me. I asked my husband if they could visit. "Yes, your sisters are welcome," Eros told me, "but are you sure you can trust them? You are living a life far richer than they can even imagine. They can come; but my love, I beseech you, be careful. What we have is precious and will never come again in this life."

His words went in one ear and out the other. Why would my sisters want to harm me? I dispatched an invite and they arrived forthwith, eager to see my palace and meet my husband. I never dreamed they would set themselves against me, but I'd never been jealous. Always the most beautiful, everyone had been jealous of me.

I could see that the moment they arrived, my sisters were dumbfounded by my wealth. It drove a wedge between us that had probably always been there, and right away their behavior was petty. But they were my sisters and I was glad to see them. I wanted Eros to come and meet them, but he still refused to make an appearance in daylight.

"Psyche, where's this sexy husband of yours? Why are you keeping him from us? Are you afraid we'll steal him away?" They laughed when they said this because they knew there was no way this was ever going to happen, but the onslaught had begun. Slowly they chipped away at my confidence. The radiance I'd gained in Eros's arms began to dim and I agreed to their plot one fateful afternoon when they said, "How can you lie in the arms of someone you've never even seen? Aren't you afraid he's a monster? What if he's deformed? What will your children look like?"

I wish I'd been strong enough to resist them, but I wasn't. I didn't have the confidence to trust my body's instincts. That night, when my husband fell asleep, I lit an oil lamp and held it above his body. What I saw was far beyond what I could have dreamt. My husband was not a monster. He was the most beautiful man who had ever existed. I was so entranced by his beauty I didn't notice the lamp in my hand was starting to tip and then—alas—hot oil spilled from the lip onto my beloved's sleeping body. He awoke in an instant, leaping from our love bed with a curse that I had ruined everything. He fled.

Why couldn't I have trusted him? How violated he must have felt when I exposed him. How betrayed that I couldn't trust him. I set off, leaving the palace to wander until I found him or died.

I wish I could say my sisters were sorry for me, but I finally saw their true colors when they heard my husband had left me. "Maybe we can have him now," I heard them mutter behind my back. I didn't stop them when they hot-footed it to the crag where Zephyr, the West Wind, had wafted me into Eros's arms. I didn't shout *don't do it* when they leaped from the precipice. For all I knew, they would end up in his bed chamber. I had betrayed him so utterly, I wouldn't have blamed him for seeking comfort with my sisters.

But that's not what happened. Zephyr did not spirit my sisters away to a palace with gold walls and invisible servants. He was nowhere in sight when they crashed on the rocks below when all the bones in their bodies shattered and their brains leaked out to stain the rocks for all eternity.

I prayed to Aphrodite for help. I didn't know then that she

was the cause of my despair. Who but the Goddess of Love could help me? I prayed to her, the most beautiful woman in the world, despite what the silly humans who'd wrecked my life thought, and she heard me. "I'll help you, Psyche, but there's a cost."

"What is it!" I pleaded. "I'll do anything!"

When I saw what she wanted me to do, my heart quaked. Aphrodite brought me to a room filled with grains and leaped on me. She threw me to the ground and pinned my face in the mountain of seeds. Wheat, barley, poppy lentils, millet—millions of seeds—and demanded I sort them all by morning. She released me and stormed off. I sat up, and scraping seeds off my face that men had once traveled miles to see, began the task, even though I knew I had no hope of completing it.

Out of the corner of my eye, I saw them, a stream of ants moving toward the seed mountain. I was in their way—they flowed right around me, rejoining each other to ascend the pile. They began sorting barley from wheat and millet from poppy, working diligently all night without stopping. In the morning, when Aphrodite came to gloat at my failure, the seeds were sorted. Aphrodite was furious when she saw what the ants had accomplished.

"I don't know how you managed it, but you're not off the hook yet," she told me. "I'll not help you find Eros just yet. First, you're going to have to bring me the wool of the golden sheep, and if you think grabbing a handful of fleece from a sheep is going to be easy, think again. These sheep are vicious and have poisonous bites. You'll be sure to be trounced and gored, but if you want my help you have no choice, so get on with it."

I made my way to the sheep's mountain with my head down, dragging my spirit behind me. There was no way I could get close enough without being gored and maimed. Eros probably wouldn't want me anymore after what I'd done anyway. I stood on the cliff above the river and resolved to jump. My story would end here.

Just then I heard a sound rising up from the riverbank. It was a reed, green and pliant, making sweet music. I was stunned when it spoke to me. "Psyche, even though you are burdened, don't pollute my clear water with your death. I'll tell you how to get the fleece of the golden sheep. Don't approach them now when they're fired up and ornery from the midday sun's heat. Wait until the day has cooled off and they rest in the river breeze. Hide in the nearby grove and when the sheep have rested and gone on their way, shake the foliage and you will loosen the golden fleece."

This is what I did and the reed's prophecy came true. The angry sheep slept and rested in the shady grove. When they rose and departed, the thickets were draped with golden fleece. I gathered it up and returned to Aphrodite.

Aphrodite was not pleased. Let's just say if looks could kill, I'd be dead. "You are showing more fortitude and persistence than I expected," she glowered at me. "Either that or someone is taking pity on you and helping you out. No one will come to your aid with this next task, Psyche. That would be a death wish."

With those words, Aphrodite gave me a crystal vessel and told me I was to climb a black mountain to the source of the River Styx and fill it with water. The rocks were slick with mold and monstrous serpents hissed at me as I climbed. I was sure I would slip—I did slip—but somehow I kept going until my hands were bloody from gripping the rocks. Finally I fell backward and landed on my tailbone on an outcropping of rock, the wind knocked out of me. For the second time, I contemplated throwing myself off the cliff but just as I was about to do it, Zeus sent an eagle to me. The eagle took the crystal bowl in its beak and flew to the River Styx's source, filling it with water. My third task was complete. I returned to Aphrodite, sure she would now help me. But no, her heart was still hard. She set me a task she knew there was no coming back from. I was to journey to the Underworld with a small box she handed to me with a smirk. "You must ask Persephone to fill this box with some of her beauty."

I knew it was hopeless and I would die. I would never see my husband again and he would never know how sorry I was that I hadn't trusted him. Still, if I hadn't been so curious, I never would have known how strong I was, or how many friends I had to help me. Even if they were only ants, reeds, and an eagle, they were friends nevertheless. But even with friends, I couldn't find the Underworld. It was time to give up. Aphrodite had just handed me the box and shooed me away, probably because she knew this time there was no way I could succeed. I would take my own life. This time no one would stop me. I walked across a plain until I came to a tower. This would be the place. With heavy feet, I climbed the tower, walking out onto the battlement to look out over the ruins of my dreams.

I swear my hands were on the stone balustrade. I had swung one leg over. I was going to do it. There was no going back now. This was the end of everything, or at least me. But a voice spoke—the tower. This is what it told me:

Psyche, don't give up yet. There is a way for you to go to the Underworld and survive. Go to Lacedaemon and seek out the place called Taenarus. That's where you'll find the entrance to the Underworld. It's a pathless route and you'll have to be wily as well as brave. Once you cross the threshold you're committed. There will be no way out. And you need honey cakes. Make sure you carry honey cakes in your hands and two gold coins in your mouth. You'll know what to do with them when the time comes.

I had seen a lot in my young life, slept with the most beautiful man in existence, touched the golden fleece, and been aided by ants and eagles. How could I not try? I took the tower at its word and swung my leg back over the balustrade, walked back down the circular stairs and made my way to Taenarus in Lacedaemon. There I found the entrance to the Underworld. I stepped through the threshold without hesitation.

Remaining silent just as the tower had advised me, I walked past the old man driving a mule loaded with sticks who begged me with his eyes to help him carry his burden. I walked past the dead man flailing in the river and the old women weavers who moaned how much their backs ached. The tower had told me these people would try to divert me from my purpose. I must remain committed, walk on toward Persephone with the small box in my hand and ask her for the impossible: a measure of her beauty.

I knew right away what to do with the honey cakes when I saw Cerberus, the three-headed dog, watchman of Orcus. I tossed him the cakes in my left hand and dodged past while he gobbled them up in his three mouths. The gold coins under my tongue were for Charon, who would ferry me across the River Styx where I would finally face Persephone. I opened my mouth and he took one. Not a word passed between us as he poled us across the black river.

And there she was, Persephone, Goddess of the Underworld. I had expected her to be terrifying, but she was really not much older than me. She was beautiful and smelled like flowers. She spun a pomegranate in her palm and flicked it open with a fingernail, silently offering me a seed. No, I said. I had heard her story. Even though I couldn't see how I'd ever make it back to the world above, I preferred to die trying rather than surrender my soul to Hades.

Finally, Persephone spoke. "Why have you come, Psyche?"

Somehow I found my voice and tucking my quivering hands behind my back I said, with some audacity, "I've come for your beauty secrets, Persephone. Aphrodite needs them. Would you be so kind as to put them here in this box?"

I held out the box thinking she'd strike it from my hand and then strike me dead, but to my eternal shock, she laughed. "You are a bold one, aren't you? Well, I guess I'll just have to give you what you want, though I'm not sure why Aphrodite needs any beauty secrets from me. I let myself go down here in Hades. I could use some of hers."

She took the box from my hand. "You're quite a beauty yourself. Enough to make Aphrodite jealous." I think she winked, but I said nothing. To my astonishment, she had filled the box with something that I couldn't quite see, closed the lid, and handed it back to me. "Don't forget to give Charon that gold coin in your cheek. And good luck getting past Cerberus. He's been a ravenous bastard lately. Hope you kept some of those honey cakes." And with that, Persephone turned and disappeared into an acrid, smoking landscape. I could hear laughter, demonic and delighted, a man's deep voice, as I walked away.

Charon took the second coin from my teeth and ferried me back across the River Styx. I diverted Cerberus with the honey cakes I'd saved in my right hand. I was on my way. The pathless path seemed a bit more clear. There was a faint light appearing before my feet as I walked on. The ground began to slope upwards. And then something rattled in the box. I had almost forgotten it, so intent on making it back to the light. My curiosity got the best of me. I opened the box. All that was in it was a strange, dreary sleep, a Stygian stupor. Someone screamed. The light at the end of the tunnel in front of me flared and then died. I fell to the ground and was overtaken by a sleep from which I could not awaken.

But Eros had not forgotten me. My beautiful, winged man. All this time he'd been recovering from his wounds in his mother's house. She cosseted him and kept him locked up so he wouldn't come after me, but eventually, he healed and escaped. He flew out the window and he found me. Lying on the pathless path on the way from the Underworld he found me in death's sleep. He's the one who told me what he did. I don't remember of course, but I felt it, the moment he drew the stupor out of me, Persephone's sleep, and put it back in the box, pricking me this time with an arrow to awake me, rather than make me Aphrodite's plaything. I awoke with my head to his heart, joining him in joyful tears. He swooped me up and together we flew to Aphrodite.

The Goddess of Love was not pleased. I've said it before and I'll say it again. Aphrodite was not pleased. "Eros, you cannot marry this girl," she insisted. "You are a god and she is a lowly mortal. Think of how ugly she'll be in a few years when you are still in your prime."

"Mother, I love you but I've had enough of your machinations. I'm taking this to Zeus." And that is what my Eros did. Now Zeus was always looking for a favor, so he consented to our marriage if my husband would give him a heads-up whenever a beautiful young maiden wandered close to Olympus. Zeus even had Hermes convene all the gods and made a public statement of his approval of our union, which royally pissed off Aphrodite. There was no way she could renege on her oath now. But Zeus must have known her ways, he must have known she'd be out for revenge, for he gave us one last gift. There, before all the gods, he offered me a goblet of ambrosia. I drank it and became immortal. I married my Eros as a true equal.

A banquet followed. As soon as we could, my husband and I retired from the revels and fell into each other's arms. This time, with the lights on, we gave ourselves to each other. I loved to look at him with his eyes closed as he writhed underneath me. And when he opened them and spun me over onto my back in a gyre of rapture, we knew our baby's name. Voluptas, child of rapture, was born not long after our wedding and she was a merry baby. The celebration is still going on if you'd like to join us.

After I finish the story my eyes wander across the water and up, drawn by the smaller palm on the right that's been flourishing all this time in the taller palm's shadow. The tall palm grew *too* tall—the wind storm that ripped through the park as I was telling "The Descent of Inanna" tore off its crown. Now it's just a bare trunk.

The Tree of Knowledge has been decapitated.

New life could sprout from the crown. Trees can do that. Or the tree could fall into the pond and become a shelter for fish and crabs and insects and invisible microorganisms.

Not growing tall, the small palm has remained sturdy. The small tree remembers how to resource its roots. The Tree of Life has been here all along.

The Fall is natural, but so is the Rising. That's what we forgot when we believed Eve sinned when she gave in to the serpent's temptation and ate the apple from the Tree of Life, at the beginning of the myth we are living out now. The trees reflected in the pond have no roots.

If you are born on this earth you deserve to be here. Nobody needs to be saved or redeemed. Root yourself between sky and earth and just be.

CHAPTER 12
THE WHITE DOVE

⊚

R EVERIE COMES quickly now. I make my acknowledgments to the water and settle in and sink so deep I have no memory of what happened until 'ulili's bright cry brings me back to my stone seat. I watch the wandering tatler bob and strut. It pauses for a moment and looks directly at me. Have I become a part of its daily routine, familiar and safe? The little bird doesn't seem to fear me. I silently thank it before it disappears deeper into the marshy area beyond the ponds where I haven't walked because I have the feeling what looks like solid ground will prove to be more water.

A splash draws my eyes left. The fish are feeding on the bottom with their tails out of the water. On the right pond, nary a ripple. Then, as if they've been waiting for a witness, a courting fish couple swims from left to right across the newly created canal and disappears into the murk.

I sink into the reflection of one of the scrubby shrubs that line the right pond's edge. Has it been there all along? How have I not seen it? Mesmerized, my eyes go soft and I notice many reflections, including several palms that are a good 50 feet away. The water is perfectly still so there is nothing to break the illusion they are just as real as the real trees.

My eyes take me in and out of dimensions. In the far right corner, two eyes upon me. I lean forward to push myself up and as I stand, I notice right where my toes were, a fat crab. He's been wedged tight all this time and is happily shoving invisible food with his tiny filament-thin claws into his mouth. My gaze does not disturb him.

Yesterday on the way to the ceremony, two white doves sliced open the air in front of my windshield as if they were cutting a hole in the sky for me to pass through into another reality. One second more and they would have splattered on my windshield and been one of those piles of blood and feathers on the side of the road that always makes me so sad, scavenged by mongoose.

I see mourning doves here often, but *never* white doves. I was focused on getting on with the ceremony, so I didn't absorb their significance, but now I think of how Noah sent a dove into the air to see if the flood waters had subsided, and how the dove came back to the ark with an olive branch in its mouth to let him know the earth was still friendly to humans. The ceremony has quickened. I feel it move inside me. I watch it ripple across the surface of the pond like an unborn baby's kick. I am in unknown territory. I can be a guide but at this point, I am not in charge of anything. All I can do is offer you a story, the second half of "The Descent of Inanna," what happened after Dumuzi had fled his fate in the form of a slippery snake.

DUMUZI'S DREAM

Laying among the rushes, asleep to the soft rattle of wind shaking the barley, Dumuzi, the sweet shepherd, husband to Inanna, Queen of Heaven, had a vision so terrifying it hurtled him back to the waking world. In a cold sweat, he called out for his little sister, Geshtinanna, who sang many songs and knew the meaning of words and dreams. Geshtinanna rushed to his side and this is what he told her:

"Geshtinanna, I'm so terrified! I dreamed I was laying in rushes so thick I couldn't move. The breath is almost crushed out of me. When I see one single reed trembling for me, I know I am a goner. And then, a double-growing reed, first one, then another, is removed. Who took them away? I couldn't see anything."

"I'm in a wooded grove. The trees are so tall they block the light. Terror, pure terror. Water is poured over my holy heart. The bottom of my churn drops away. My drinking cup falls from its peg. My shepherd's crook disappears. And then I hear a voice:"

'When the fire is put out on your holy hearth,
The sheepfold will become a house of desolation.

When the bottom of your churn drops away,
You will be held by the galla.

When your driving cup falls from its peg,
You will fall to the earth, onto your mother's knees.'

"Sister, what could this all mean? I beg you, tell me. I will die from the terror. Please help me escape."

Geshtinanna paled when she heard her brother's vision. She knew she was speaking his death sentence as she interpreted the dream. She didn't spare him. "Dear brother, I fear the worst. The galla are coming to take you to the Underworld. We must flee."

Sure enough, the galla came. The siblings watched them from a hill. Dumuzi took flight again and hid, but the galla caught up with Geshtinanna. "We will offer you the gifts of water and grain if you will give your brother up," they said, but she refused. The galla tortured her, tearing clothes and pouring pitch into her vulva. Geshtinanna remained silent, loyal to her brother.

Onward the galla traveled. They came to the home of a friend of Dumuzi's and made the same offer. This friend was more afraid than Geshtinanna and not so loyal. "Yes," he said, giving up his friend right away. "Dumuzi is hiding in the grass near here."

The galla looked for him but Dumuzi was not there. "He's hiding in the small plants," the friend told them when they came back, but when they looked in the small plants they did not find Dumuzi.

Finally, the friend revealed where Dumuzi really was. "You will find him in the ditches of Arali."

The galla left this faithless friend and continued onward to Arali. That is where they found Dumuzi.

Dumuzi wept and wailed in self-pity and genuine terror to no avail. The galla bound his hands and neck and beat him to a pulp. Raising his bound arms Dumuzi cried out to Utu, the god of justice. "Utu! I offered gifts at your temple! Change me into a gazelle so I can escape!"

Utu heard his plea and remembered all the gifts Dumuzi had brought him. He did as Dumuzi asked. In the form of a gazelle, Dumuzi bound away, hiding in the house of an old woman named Belili.

But he couldn't escape the galla. Nobody can. The demons of the Underworld are mighty. They cornered him there and just as they were about to nab him, Dumuzi pulled another trick out of his hat and somehow escaped again, streaking over the plains to his sister's sheepfold.

When Geshtinanna found him hiding, wretched and trembling, she wept. Where was her brother the golden shepherd?

She knew he'd never make sweet music again on his reed flute or shine on his throne like the sun. She dropped and groaned into the earth. Her grief was a garment that covered the horizon.

The galla climbed into the sheepfold and ignored her prostrate body. It was Dumuzi they wanted. Without a word, they pierced one of his cheeks with a nail. The other they struck with a shepherd's crook. They smashed the churn and shattered the drinking cup. He was seized and stripped of his royal garments.

> The churn was silent. No milk was poured.
> The cup was shattered. Dumuzi was no more.
> The sheepfold was given to the winds.
>
> Gone is my husband, my sweet husband.
> Gone is my love, my sweet love.
> My beloved has been taken from the city.
> O, you flies of the steppe.
>
> My beloved bridegroom has been taken from me
> Before I could wrap him with a proper shroud.
>
> The wild bull lives no more.

Sirtur, Dumuzi's mother grieved also. Geshtinanna grieved. Everyone was lost in grief. Finally, Geshtinanna and Inanna found each other. "Is he really gone?" Geshtinanna implored the Queen of Heaven, her brother's wife.

When Inanna saw the depth of Geshtinanna's grief she knew she must speak gently. "Yes, Geshtinanna, he is gone."

Geshtinanna's wail cracked the clouds open.

"I swear if I knew where he was I'd take you to him," Inanna told the grieving sister. She, too, wanted to find him so she could give him the proper funeral rites, but there was no body.

As they were speaking, Inanna and Geshtinanna were unaware they had witnesses. Two holy flies had been attracted to the scent of death around them and overheard their conversation. *They* knew where Dumuzi was, the divine shepherd, consort of the Queen of Heaven. Flying to Inanna's ear they buzzed, "What will you give us if we tell you where he is?"

Inanna considered. What would a fly want? Aha! And then she knew. "If you tell me where Dumuzi is I will let you frequent the taverns and dwell among the talk and songs of sages and minstrels."

The flies were dumbfounded. Inanna was offering them backstage passes to the most exclusive clubs of the day. They would get to be up and close and personal with the stars. Hear all the gossip. "Deal!" they shouted together.

Now if you think this sounds strange, why would anyone care about eavesdropping on a bunch of drunks, let me ask you to reconsider. I personally have known quite a few barroom mystics slurring truth sideways and sometimes falling to the ground from the weight of it. Sometimes truth can only be borne by intoxication.

And if that doesn't convince you, remember, some of the greatest mystics hung out in taverns: Dylan Thomas, Jack Kerouac, Shakespeare. And while we don't know for sure if Rumi and Hafiz were advocating actual drunkenness in their poems, they certainly knew that intoxication was one pathway to God. Imagine being a fly on a wall when Shakespeare and Ben Jonson were drinking madeira in Cheapside. Now you can see why the flies were so excited.

I digress. The flies kept their end of the bargain. "Lift your eyes to the edge of the steppe," they told Inanna, "Go to Arali. You will find Dumuzi there."

At once, Inanna and Geshtinanna set out. Together they found Dumuzi in Arali like the flies said they would.

Dumuzi was weeping. No surprise. In fact, he was crying

his eyes out. He was so blinded by his own tears he didn't recognize his own wife, his Queen, until she spoke.

"Dumuzi," Inanna said with some tenderness. He had not mourned her, but he was still beautiful and she had loved him once. Better to get it over quickly. "You will go to the Underworld half the year. Your sister, Geshtinanna, has offered to take your place the other half."

Dumuzi looked up in bewilderment. Was it true? Was Geshtinanna willing to do this for him? *Yes,* she nodded. Geshtinanna was loyal-hearted. She would go.

"On the day you are called, you'll be taken. On the day Geshtinanna is called, you'll be set free."

Inanna pronounced their sentence, the selfish brother and the faithful sister, but it was not her that decided their fate. She placed them in the hands of the eternal. She had come back from the Underworld. It was true what the galla said, she was marked.

A voice cried out, anonymous in the wilderness: *Holy Ereshkigal! Great is your renown!*

CHAPTER 13
RUIN MEDICINE

TODAY I SIT at the base of the bridge. If I was sitting on a human brain this would be the amygdala, the fear center. I think of Bashō's haiku:

Old pond...
a frog jumps in
water's sound

I turn my head expecting to see the wandering monk himself, but it's the black-crowned night heron from the first day of the ceremony. *Where have you been all this time? Wise one, I've been looking for you. You've been hidden in the long grass, watching me—or not. Living your own life where I exist in an alternate reality. Yet here we are...*

Today our realities are coming closer. Today this wild, red-eyed bird with the extravagant plume that looks like a tail sprouting from its feather crown, has decided to hunt ten feet away from me, right out in the open. He freezes when he realizes I see him, but I am just as exposed. *You are safe,* I whisper, hoping he will go on hunting.

Quietly, the bird pivots on stick-thin legs and steps into a patch of long grass just large enough to hide his body when he folds his legs under him and lowers to the ground. I can see the top of his head. Red eyes fix on me through the green camouflage. Look away. Give him space.

He rises and steps out of the grass. A memory rises up from the lost river inside my body: *If I lay here on this cot in the corner, if I don't meet his eyes, he'll stop pacing, fall asleep, pass out drunk; the path to the door will be clear and I will be able to slip out of the cabin, my escape covered by the sound of the waterfall.*

I listen to the bird stalk (watch out Big Papa!). My head pivots as if the wind is moving it and not my muscles and skeleton. He flattens and thrusts forward his feathered trunk, striding through the water, his beak slashing like a knife through silk. Freeze, dash, freeze, the pattern. I know it well.

Finally, he disappears again in the scrub growing at the Great Wall's edge, almost as if he had slipped between the cracks like the mongoose I'd tracked the other day.

If only there was a wonderland where all the animals of the world could escape to safety. Extinction would be extinct and maybe we'd miss them all so much we'd summon them back with love spells. As my mind contemplates the wall and the possibility of another dimension between the cracks, another heron appears, then another, and I am awestruck by the presence of three black-crowned night herons until I realize I just lost track of the first one each time it froze and they moved again. There is only one heron. It is enough.

Auku'u,
mahālo for allowing me to watch you
stride and slash the still water
your beak the grim reaper's
merciful hook.

Plumed warrior,
mahālo for showing how death
is necessary
for us all to go on living,
the fish struggling in your gullet
not a punishment
but natural law.

We are all shapeshifters
reforming, remembering.

When it's my time to die
I hope I remember your red eyes
blazing between grass blades,
how you swallowed the fish
without hesitation.

Today you have shown me
I don't have to stay frozen
for more than the few seconds it takes
to know I am safe, the past
no longer dwells
in my body.

HO'OKUKĀLA, A PROCLAMATION

Depression—the dark side of empathy—I've been your recep-
tacle for too long. I proclaim a boundary between me and the
world's denied and unexpressed feelings. A Great Wall patrolled
by a black-crowned night heron who strides through the water
like a Fury, stabbing the pain with its beak and swallowing it
whole—but the wall is permeable.

I will not let my heart harden. I will watch the refugees struggling to reach shore in rafts and cry, let my heart break when it looks in the photographed eyes of starving children, hug my friends, smile at my neighbors who don't make eye contact, make offerings to my ancestors and their unfulfilled dreams.

I am the result of my lineage, but their losses and longings will no longer dwell inside me. In exchange, I'll do my best to give my own losses back to Earth the way the fish give their lives to auku'u. I'll be brave and follow my longing to the land's edge. If called, I will leap.

The water is deep—and there are sharks. One day I won't make it back to shore, but until then I'll do what my body has always known how to do—keep swimming, keep listening to the Great Below.

Once in a ceremony, in line to make my offering at a shrine to Tlazteotl, the Huastec goddess known as the Filth-Eater, I found myself weeping so hard I almost fell to the ground.

I had no idea I had this undetonated landmine of tears inside me. I sobbed beyond my limits, letting the tears soften the calcified places inside where pain had hardened me. I probably *would* have dropped to the ground if the elder behind me hadn't placed a hand on the back of my heart. She offered support, not comfort. She knew better than to do anything that would staunch my tears. Her hand on my heart let me know not only were they necessary, they were *needed*.

That day I wept far beyond myself.

HI'ILAWE

Hi'ilawe was a beautiful maiden who lived long ago in Waipi'o. One day when she and her lover Kakalaoa ventured into the back of the valley, they heard an 'elepaio chirp. This bird's call was considered such a bad omen the two froze and would not let go of each other. Unable to stop weeping, Hi'ilawe became a waterfall and Kakalaoa became the large boulder at the base in the pool below, and thus are joined as long as this world lasts.

Hollowed out by tears, tempered by ruin, true healing begins. In pua'aehuehu, Kīlau Pueo, the fern of Ruin, frees us from bondage to our traumas through releasing our unexpressed emotions. This makes it sound easy. It's not. Ruin is a hot, but glorious mess. It's throwing a plate of spaghetti on the wall when your family is bitching and moaning. My grandmother actually did that. My dad told me when her shocked kids and husband looked up and saw spaghetti strands stuck to the wall everyone, including my grandmother, started laughing. She let that rage out. It may not always turn so quickly into comic relief for everyone, but ruin is still necessary. Sometimes the only medicine is to be destroyed— or destroy ourselves, what can't be tolerated any longer. I don't know why my grand-mother was angry enough to throw a platter of spaghetti on the wall, but she didn't run from it, and in her honor I vow to do the same, and invite you to do the same. As Ke'oni says, allow anger to be friendly. Negotiate with ruin. This is something I've been doing for the past 14 years since I was diagnosed with the autoimmune disease ulcerative colitis.

Ulcerative colitis is a chronic diagnosis, meaning I'll sup-posedly have it for the rest of my life. The process of accepting this as a possibility has required surrender on multiple levels. It's a very fine line between having hope I will be cured and accepting I may not be. I have been delusional at times, deny-ing what was happening in my body to the point where I've collapsed near what felt like death and been hospitalized.

One level of surrender surprised me more than others. One night during a two week stay in Hilo hospital, high on prednisone and morphine, Coltrane's *A Love Supreme*, in my headphones, I realized my insistence on "healing myself" as the holistic health movement insisted I could do, was a form of self-torture, and even more than that, an indicator of my inflated ego that pointed to what needed to die in order to bring me closer to God. What I realized was that ulcerative colitis was trying to teach me to surrender to a greater power, not dominate what that greater power had given me, a body to experience life on Earth. For me, at that time, that meant accepting that the drugs being pumped through IVs and a port in my chest were the medicine I needed. Thank you, Coltrane. I don't believe I would have had this epiphany without you. And thank you to the nurse's aide who sat with me in the night, the one who told me that her family had gone back to Kalapana after Pele consumed their house in 1991, and built a new home on the lava.

I cried when I realized how much I'd prolonged my body's agony by not taking medication, ignoring my symptoms multiple times for months until my body couldn't take anymore, forcing my surrender in a hospital bed.

Ke'oni says tears are a legitimate sacrifice. I know that now. So is inadequacy. Maybe I did summon ulcerative colitis to me because I felt inadequate as a human, but I don't worry about that now. I'm not trying so hard to fix myself, I let life move through me how it wants and do my best to put up the lightest sail to catch the breeze.

And what was on the other side of that waterfall of tears? My invocation. These words, the clear tone of a temple bell tolling the sun's eventual death as Earth turns.

Right before I pass back through the Great Wall a local man stops me and signals to something in his hand. "Is this yours?" he asks. I see it's a glasses case. "No," I answer.

"You going by the front desk?" he asks.

"Yes."

Without another word, he passes it off to me like a relay baton. "Have a beautiful day," he says and walks into the sunset.

"You too," I say to his back as he disappears into the lava. I leave the glasses at the desk on my way out. I drive home under a rainbow, both ends planted in the mountain above me. The sky seems clearer. I can see a long way into the distance.

CHAPTER 14
THE WATER OF LIFE

◎

"Verily, verily I say unto thee, except a man be born of water
and of the spirit, he cannot enter into the Kingdom of God."

John 3:5

THE FLOW between the ponds is restored. Left and right
reunited.

This was not what I expected based on my first
encounter walking in the park today. As I stepped off the ramp
onto the gravel, my eyes were drawn up by a shriek, five white
egrets pinwheeling out of a palm tree. Then I saw what had
startled them—a drone. No operator in sight.

My first impulse was war. I cursed the man and his drone,
but Big Papa didn't swim away when I sat down at the water's
edge and sought his gaze. We made eye contact for a long time
until two females approached. He pivoted and swung into the
center where it was too dark for my eyes to follow.

The 'ulili is here, perched on the bridge bobbing head and
tail. Some of my sadness and anger dissipate when it doesn't

fly away. It bobs and dips as I watch fish nibble on the rocks in the new channel connecting the ponds.

Yet I feel dull, sluggish, and foolish. This whole ceremony could be one big kapu. I am not from this place. Who am I to think I have the right to converse with this land and water? I am just a stupid haole. I have no right to be here.

Earth needs more from me—from us. That's the kind of thinking that will only keep the cycle of colonization going, a closed loop. I need to open it, even though I'm ashamed, so I risk looking foolish and crazy and wait until the wind blows a certain way or a bird peeps, some sign that seems like it might be an invitation. And though I don't receive any sign I recognize, a thought comes to me that takes me out of my pattern, stretching my mind, opening the closed loop I despair of transcending.

As a noun, a loop signifies a closed circle—we are contained by the word in a cycle beyond our control. As a verb "to loop" allows us the possibility of agency. If we loop fast enough to gain the velocity, centrifugal forces emerge to fling us into the next spiral, hopefully expanded by our journey, although perhaps our only true agency is in surrendering, taking that leap into the whirlpool that will either drown us or spit us out somewhere downriver.

In this way we can learn from grief and carry its lessons of surrender and bravery with us when we rise from the banks and walk back to human company to share the story of how we survived, birthing more beauty. Grief, if we allow it to move us, is fertile.

Looping back, the thought I mentioned came as a memory—something I read about when researching the text of "The Descent of Inanna," preserved in history on stone tablets carved by an unknown scribe almost 5,000 years ago. Although I told them on separate days, the story of Inanna's descent and rise back to the great heaven actually ends with "Dumuzi's

Dream," in which we hear of how Dumuzi tries unsuccessfully to escape his punishment for not properly mourning Inanna. I separated the story because to me they seemed distinct. If told continuously, we go right from hearing how Dumuzi slithers away in snake form, to a detailed account of his capture that begins with him dreaming of the event and appealing to his sister Geshtinanna to save him. However, there is a space between them, a space held by 20 lines scholars tell us are somewhere out there on missing stone tablets.

What's going on in that space? Does time exist there? Do the missing lines know 5,000 years have passed since they were first etched in stone? Has the story changed, the way time changes everything on Earth? And even more intriguing, what is the potential of that space? Is it really missing even if it's not etched in stone?

"The Descent of Inanna" was composed in Sumer, the first great agricultural civilization that birthed the Western world that has culminated in the industrial capitalism that dominates our planet today. We know from their stories that ancient agricultural societies viewed sacrifice as essential to ensure the land's fertility. Something must be offered to the land in exchange for what we take by clearing and plowing, for taming the wild. We have forgotten this.

Cultures that remember have traditionally made offerings of prayers, smoke, flowers, and blood—animal and human. Contact broken, industrial agriculture rapes the land, gives nothing in exchange, and doesn't even see it as alive. Earth is a thing to be used for human advantage, incapable of having wants or needs or dreams of her own, unable to feel pain. So why does it matter if we scrape, bomb, and drill our way into her? Animals are tortured in factory farms. We eat terror and utter hopelessness on a regular basis. The worst is that it's not even a secret anymore. People know and still do it anyway. We are numb. Stuffing empathy down with racks of ribs and chicken wings.

I'm not writing this to cast blame or shame. More and more individuals are doing the necessary work required to change our societies from the inside out, but trauma healing is required on a mass scale in order for our human cultures to come back into right relationship with Earth. First, we need to collectively acknowledge how traumatized we are before we begin that journey, difficult to do when our civilization's founding, the Book of Genesis, tell us humans were put on the earth in order to have dominion over all God's creatures. By human, I mean man specifically, by "our civilization" I mean Western. Fortunately, there are still cultures today founded on other stories.

Not every culture has lived by farming and domesticating animals. Hunter-gatherer cultures are generally not the cultures one reads about in the history books, at least when I was in school in the 1970s and 80s, because they didn't leave behind grand pyramids or lost cities. They did not write things down because they were on the move. Their wisdom was inside them. They knew it by heart.

Luckily, when they eventually came in contact with literate cultures some of their stories were written down because most of these cultures have been wiped from the planet through the horrors of colonialism.

Often nomadic, hunter-gatherers lived from what the land offered: animals, fruit, seeds, berries, and lived in dwellings made from hides or woven reeds that fell apart as the weather had its way with them, rotting back to Earth. They were people who slept on the ground and left little to no trace of their passing.

Genesis is past its peak. Eve has been rattling her cage for quite some time now, and in many spots on Earth has escaped. Lilith is wreaking vengeance. The story it generated— industrial capitalism—is coming to an end. Humanity could end with it, maybe not in the next 100 years, but it's unlikely we'll last for the next seven generations, a measurement of how to determine right action according to indigenous North Americans. If we go on extracting resources at the rate we are now, dumping plastics into the sea, blasting the tops off mountains, poisoning our water with toxic chemicals, and refusing to offer our bodies back into the food chain as compost for new life, we won't continue. We pump our dead with preservative chemicals and seal them in plush coffins. Sometimes we burn them and seal the ashes in urns. What kind of ancestors are these? No wonder we are haunted. We can't even let the dead be dead. Meanwhile, Earth is starving.

"And what rough beast... / slouches towards Bethlehem to be born?" Yeats prophesied just over a hundred years ago.

If we are being dreamed and the stories are a clue to what beast is dreaming us, what does it mean when the story we can see all around us is imploding? If, as the Hawaiians say, power is in the present moment, what would happen if I invite another kind of story into this ceremony, a story from a lineage more ancient than the agricultural—one from our hunter-gatherer ancestors?

One came to me recently through the air in the voice of storyteller Jay Leeming. It's called "The Oldest Boy," and I'm going to tell it now to this pond and to the space created by those 20 missing lines, that gap between "The Descent of Inanna" and "Dumuzi's Dream."

THE OLDEST BOY

A long time ago, when people were first figuring out how to live in this world, nobody slept in air-tight houses or bought their family's food in a grocery store. People built their homes from whatever the earth gave them. In the far north, there was a village where the people lived together in one stone lodge, gathering close together in winter to keep warm.

One winter when it was time for everyone to seal themselves in the lodge to weather the bitter cold, the elders looked around and realized they didn't have enough food to survive the entire winter. They made a decision. In order to conserve resources and energy, they would sleep most of the day, leaving most of the food for the children.

Now, the children didn't think much of the adults sleeping all day like hibernating bears. They actually thought it was pretty fun. They played games all day and enjoyed nobody telling them what to do. The adults would wake up around dusk to eat a little soup and check on everyone. Most of the time the oldest boy was in charge. He was one of those boys that came to leadership naturally, brash and a little bossy. He organized games for the little kids and when the adults woke up they were glad to see nobody was alarmed at their long slumber.

One day the oldest boy gathered all the kids to him and said, "I've thought of a new game. Wanna play?" Of course, the kids said yes. "What's the game called?" they clamored.

Preening like a bird, the oldest puffed up his chest and said, "The game is called calling in the spirits." The little kids looked up at him in awe. He liked this feeling. He began to sing:

Oh spirit, come to me. Oh spirit, come to me. I call upon the spirit of the soul of the sea.

Oh spirit, come to me. Oh spirit, come to me. I call upon the spirit of the soul of the sea.

Oh spirit, come to me. Oh spirit, come to me. I call upon the spirit of the soul of the sea.

As soon as he stopped, the stones on the ground began to

levitate, whirling around the ice lodge. All of the kids were impressed and a little terrified. The oldest boy told them, "Don't tell the grown-ups what happened when they wake up. This is *our* secret."

"We won't tell," they promised, but of course, they couldn't keep such a huge secret. All it took was one question from a grown-up, "What do you do all day while we're asleep?" and they all spilled the beans.

Now, the adults at that time took things like levitating stones seriously. They called the oldest boy to them and asked him what was going on. "Show us this game," they said with some concern, and the oldest boy repeated his song, three times:

Oh spirit, come to me. Oh, spirit, come to me. I call upon the spirit of the soul of the sea.

Oh spirit, come to me. Oh, spirit, come to me. I call upon the spirit of the soul of the sea.

Oh spirit, come to me. Oh, spirit, come to me. I call upon the spirit of the soul of the sea.

The oldest boy was excited to impress the elders. But nothing happened. The stones on the lodge floor stayed put. As the oldest boy stood there in front of the adults, feeling pretty foolish, they all heard a great bellowing outside the lodge. Without even thinking about it, the adults scooped up the oldest boy and tossed him out toward that awful sound. Before he could even hit the ice, he was caught in a polar bear's paw, who smacked him through the air to a walrus, who caught him on a tusk. The polar bear and walrus took off with him into the white wilderness, playing catch with the oldest boy: paw to tusk, polar bear to walrus, back and forth and back and forth until they reached the place where the bone-crunching ocean met the ice, and dove right in. Polar bear to walrus, walrus to polar bear, they smacked him back and forth as they swam down, down, down, all the way to the bottom of the sea, and when they reached the bottom they passed into the land beneath the ocean where a river carried them, all the time playing toss with the oldest boy, paw to tusk, tusk to paw. Finally, they left the oldest boy on the riverbank at a bend in the river.

After a long time, the oldest boy woke up alone in the land beneath the ocean. When he got to his knees he noticed a small hut, and because there was nothing else to do, he walked toward it and entered. There was nothing in the first room, but then he noticed a door on the back wall. He opened that door and stepped into another room, and sitting at a table facing him with a blank gaze was an old, old woman. She was so old her white hair touched the floor and her face was so deeply creviced that auks could have nested in it. Most terrifying of all, she had no hands. Suddenly the oldest boy understood why her hair was so matted.

On the table next to her were three things: an ivory comb, a sealskin ribbon, and an obsidian bowl filled with water. She stared at the oldest boy as if she could see right through him. She probably could. He was speechless. Out of an unfathomable silence, the old woman spoke:

"What can *you* do for *me*?"

Without hesitation, the oldest boy walked toward the table and picked up the ivory comb. Starting at the bottom of the long, white cascade so as not to hurt her, he began to comb the old woman's hair. As he combed, sea creatures spilled out onto the hut floor, shrimp and sea lice and tiny, darting fish. The oldest boy was patient and thorough. After a time the old woman's hair began to shine as he unraveled and smoothed all the knots. But he wasn't done. He began to braid the old woman's hair, just the way his mother braided his sister's back in the lodge, and when the plait was finished he tied it off with the sealskin ribbon, and then the oldest boy held the obsidian bowl so the old woman could look at her reflection in the water. When she saw herself, just the slightest smile passed over her face. She turned and pointed to another door on the back wall and all of a sudden it opened and sea creatures spilled forth, swimming across the room into the next room and out into the river, swimming up from the land beneath the sea to fill the ocean. Seals and walruses and whales and every kind of fish you could imagine.

Before he left, the old woman instructed him on how to honor an animal's spirit. The hunter must offer the dying animal a drink of sweet water—not salt—so that it could pass over into the next world knowing the sweetness of life and come back again to feed the people. And the people must not let the dogs play with the seal's bones. They must bury them.

With this knowledge, the oldest boy left the old woman's hut. He had no idea how he was going to get home, but as soon as he stepped out of her lodge, guess who appeared? Polar bear and walrus. Again they scooped him up with paw and tusk, tossing him back and forth as they navigated the underground river back to the ocean, toying with him all the way to the surface. In one leap they were on the ice again and running— *polar bear to walrus, walrus to polar bear. Polar bear to walrus, walrus to polar bear*—until they reached the village lodge where they dumped him at the closed door and disappeared into the white horizon.

The oldest boy lay there for a long time before the villagers discovered him. When the adults, close to starving themselves now, found him, they didn't think he'd make it, but they dragged him in and set him on a sealskin next to the fire. All they had left to eat was a thin soup that could barely sustain them, but they took some of that soup to the oldest boy and held a spoonful of it to his lips, and when the soup touched his tongue he awoke. Without speaking, he stood up and walked outside the lodge. He closed his eyes and reached his arms to the sky like a great tree. Out of the sky came hundreds of birds to land on his arms like they would on branches. Covered in birds, the oldest boy felt the sun on his face and was grateful, and then he snapped the birds' necks, giving them to his people so they could break their long fast. When all the birds were eaten he made himself a gigantic harpoon, so large most men wouldn't have been able to lift it, but the oldest boy could, and with one thrust he speared a whole shoal of seals, remembering to give each one a drink of sweet water before it expired. He brought the seals back to feed the village, and he taught the villagers what the old woman had told him, how to give each seal a drink so that it could journey to the next world remembering the sweetness of life, and to keep the bones away from the dogs. From then on the villagers buried the bones on a hill overlooking the sea.

I don't know if the people of that time remembered what they learned from the oldest boy or if they forgot, but I do know it was said that if a time came when the people forgot how to harvest the life of land and sea with respect, an oldest boy would have to make the journey down to the land beneath the sea once more to comb the old woman's hair.

This story lived for a long time in the earth where it lodged in an arctic vole, who kept it safe under the ice for many years until one day the vole met its end in the teeth of a weasel. The weasel scampered off with the story as weasels do, until one day the weasel got a hankering for a fish it could hear splashing around through a hole in the ice. The weasel wanted that fish so badly it leaned over the edge hoping it could yank it up with its lightning-quick paw, but alas leaned over too far and fell into the arctic water. The weasel struggled for a long time, but the ice was too slick for it to climb out of the hole and eventually it drifted off to sleep, a merciful way to die, in the icy water. Slowly, the weasel sank, and when it reached the bottom it met a great scavenger of the sea, a crab, and was eaten up. Nobody knows how long that story lived in the crab, but in time it was caught and ended up in Pike Place Market in Seattle, Washington, and from there made its way into a crab bisque that was served to the storyteller Danny Deardorff, who told the story to Walton Stanley in the Minnesota woods, who told the story to Jay Leeming, who told it to me. And now here I am telling it to you, and I ask you, what will you do with this story?

As soon as the last words of the story leave my mouth, 'ulili pops up to my left from behind a rock. *Enjoy the story, did you?* I address the little bird. *Carry it back to Alaska when you go soon,* I whisper. *Tell the Inuit it's found a new home.*

My eyes wander to the Tree of Knowledge, so ragged now without its frond crown, and then right to the Tree of Life, short and stalwart, traveling down both trunks with my gaze to the water where I lose myself in their reflections.

This is the way to the land beneath the sea. I just know it. I can see the old woman's face from the story, her milky eyes nearly blind with cataracts turned up toward the place where the tree meets its reflection. She holds up her handless arms. Her hair is a mess. Someone needs to go down there and comb it.

Just 12 years ago when I swam over the reef in Honaunau Bay that I can see from here, the corals were much brighter. Now most of it has bleached from rising ocean temperatures. I still see the beauty in the bleached skeletons, but every time I drift over them I can't help remembering what they used to look like, and how I used to see honu, green turtles, every time I swam at Two-Step. In the past year, I've only seen two or three, and that was months ago.

On my way here every day I pass the spot where there were always honu hauled out on the sand to rest. The area is still roped off to keep people away, but I haven't seen a turtle there in almost a year.

The old woman is still sitting at her table in the hut at the river's bend in the land beneath the sea, with her ivory comb and her seal sinew ribbon and her obsidian bowl of water. What if she looks at her reflection now before someone reaches her? What if she sees her matted hair and her spirit breaks? What if she gives up on us, loses hope we will ever send an oldest boy down to comb her tangled hair, or an oldest girl to smooth her white locks to a silver sheen and braid the long length of it that reaches the floor of the hut, flowing out the door to touch the undersea river that leads to the ocean that leads to us starving on the ice? Who will hold up the obsidian mirror to see we have honored her? How will the oldest boy know we need him if we've forgotten him ourselves? This is what I see in the mirror of the water, the ponds right in front of me. It's so easy to be mesmerized by hopelessness.

I force myself to look up at the real trees, not their reflections, to the Great Wall behind them. *Power is in the present moment.*

I used to build and repair old stone walls, so I have some knowledge of the skill it took to build this wall that backs my ceremony. I can appreciate the craftsmanship and the sheer strength it took to heft these large stones and lock them into place without mortar, but today the wall makes me sad. Right now all walls make me sad. The walls on Block Island I used to repair were built when white settlers stole the land from the Manisses and began to farm it. The glacial soil was so full of stones, plows struck them, so the colonists stacked them in walls that are now considered quite picturesque and worthy of being preserved, hence my job.

But what is a wall for, really? To mark off territory. A wall says, "Mine." On Block Island, people still tell the story of how a slave could earn his freedom if he built a wall that spanned the whole island. If this story is even true, where did those freed slaves go? Their descendants certainly aren't property owners on Block Island today, though many of the descendants of the white colonizers are.

If building a wall could earn freedom, how did it feel to know that same wall would keep you out? What kind of walls does a person build inside themselves to survive that?

Walls don't just divide property, they divide the self. What kind of inner wall keeps a person from acknowledging they are taking more share of our Earth's resources, so freely shared we take them for granted and have created entire societies based on the false premise of possession? Those are the walls I want to dissolve.

When the walls come down and crumble into dust we'll know we are wind and sky, stone and the stream flowing down the mountain. We'll know we are clay and fire and touch each other the way two bodies of water join, crash becoming flow. Death will be a passage anticipated like birth.

Right before I go, I notice something new. Earlier I mentioned that a much larger fish than Big Papa & Co. cruised the pond's far side, never coming close enough for me to see it. I'd named her Queen of the Pond. Today I learn she has a consort, a King to join her in her endless progression of figure eights. I'm pretty sure they are mullet, ama'ama in Hawaiian, fish sacred to the moon goddess Hina. I have to admit, I cheated and read in a book that mullet were raised in little ponds like these to feed the ancient chiefs. I have no idea how they got here, two fish slicing through water like silver swords tracing calligraphy on a mosque dome painted deep indigo, arabesques of stars and barely remembered dreams calling us back to the holy truth. These ponds are small and far from the ocean. The King and Queen have been here all along but I couldn't see them.

The reflected trees look as real as the trees growing skyward, but a finger in the water will break them. The eye is the original mirror.

Sometimes, you can see into your own heart when you gaze into another's eyes. Sometimes when the heart's defenses collapse, the soul is revealed. Collapse may be required and exposure may be necessary, but in the end, wind and water will reclaim the wall's stones for the fire that birthed them. Someday the physical will be gone, not just you and me, but the stones, the molten lava, even the water. Between now and then every moment is a new beginning on the path to aloha mā, and though we have choices, we can't step off. Nothing is lost. The end is always a beginning.

Hawaiians tell of how Ka Mea Nāna i Hana, Creator, divided itself in order to experience itself. *Choosing* amnesia, Ka Mea Nāna i Hana set out on the path of learning everything about itself—the good and bad, the raw and dirty. The path has a guide: aloha mā, self-reflective love. By experiencing the total emotional spectrum, Creator will remember the truth, which means so will we. The experiment is still in progress.

When I look in the mirror I see a fool, an alchemist, a priestess, a queen and king, a priest and a lover. We all hold the reins to a chariot. None of us are sure yet where we're going, but we know we're not in charge. Our reins are tied to a black sphinx and a white sphinx. They are the ones who lead us toward the reckoning of justice. We ride the inward-dwelling wave of the hermit. We know to surrender to life's great wheel and are strong enough to always choose love even with our hands in the lion's mouth. We have had our worlds turned upside down and hung suspended until we finally surrendered and passed through the valley of the shadow of death to this moment now—here by the edge of two ponds filled by an unknown source of water where two shining silver fish process through their domain. They would loop in figure eights without me looking, but what if it's my attention, the aware and present gaze of one human, that sends their ripples out beyond the pond's borders to reweave the broken song-lines?

The sunset is ambrosial, a pink flush from ocean horizon to mountaintop. I am carried back up the hill by a secret aqueduct, water of a new life I have never drunk.

CHAPTER 15
DEVIL'S ISLAND

◉

I USUALLY GO to bed in the dark. Tonight when I reach the top of the stairs leading to my sleeping loft, I inexplicably flip the light switch to the left of the doorway and discover a centipede at the foot of my bed. A big one, a fat four or five inches. I'm not sure if I'm frozen in fear or amazed that my body knew to turn the light on, but I slowly make my way toward it as if it wasn't one of my greatest fears, a stinging monster whose bite is supposedly way worse than a bee's, beast with a hundred writhing legs who can leap across a room almost like it has wings. Snaky and sinister, I dread centipedes. Finding one in my bedroom is one of my worst nightmares. I don't know why I'm so calm. Maybe it's because it seems so inevitable. Here it is, right on schedule. My ceremony is bleeding out into my life up the hill where I still have a job running Paliuli Farm, tending to the Airbnb guests' needs. In a way, it's affirming, which may be why I'm not terrified.

This centipede doesn't shoot across the floor when I walk toward it. Close up, I see it's on its back, feebly wiggling its hundred legs in the air. I'm surprised how moved I am at its plight. How could I feel bad for a creature that could cause me incredible pain if it crawled into my bed like a heat-seeking missile and stung me? I've found cockroaches belly-up like this, too. When they come close to death, they flip onto their backs and can't find the strength to turn back over. Apparently, centipedes go through the same agonizing process, wriggling their hundred legs for hours until death stills them for good. Hopefully, it will be dead by morning. I can just leave it and go to sleep, right? But what if it revives in the middle of the night and creeps into bed with me? Something must be done.

I walk downstairs, shuffle through the cupboards I keep denying smell like mouse pee (not rat, please, not rat, though I've trapped a few already), pull out a handy Tupperware, and re-ascend. The centipede doesn't try to escape when the container hovers over it. *Thunk*, it's contained. I check the rim to make sure there's no way it could get out, just in case it happens to get a second wind.

Usually, I leave my phone downstairs, but tonight, with a centipede just a few feet away from me, I take it to bed. It could revive and sting me and I'll have to call 911, which I know is silly, but I'm on edge. I give into my impulse to scroll the spiritual significance of the centipede totem and discover that despite its general creepiness and painful sting, all cultures worldwide seem to view it as a sign of power, good fortune, and leadership. Sleep somehow claims me.

Early in the morning, I dream the centipede comes back to life. I get out of bed and flip the container. Still alive. While I was asleep wishing it dead, it flipped itself over, though it isn't strong enough to scurry away. Unkindly, I poke it with the plastic lid. It's clearly no threat to me. All it can do is wiggle its legs. There is no fight left in it, no gnashing of jaws in a last-ditch attempt to bite me. The centipede has surrendered.

I wish it would just die so I didn't have to move it alive.

I swear, the fear it provokes in me is so potent a shock runs through my body just scooping it up, and I still want to smash it. I'm appalled at this violence within myself. I've never even been stung by a centipede and here I am wanting to crush it just because people told me how much it could hurt me. In order to escape my base instincts, I go downstairs to brew a cup of tea. What else had I read last night about centipedes? They are superb hunters and love dust and warmth, hence their attraction to beds where dust-releasing humans radiate body heat. They come out at night in search of water. If you see one in your house, there are probably many.

Unnerved by this fact, but soothed by my cup of white tea, I go back upstairs with an empty cracker box and slip the thin cardboard lip under the centipede who disappears into the dark without protest.

Walking to a shady spot in the yard, I tilt the box. The centipede slides out, wiggles under a clump of grass and stops moving. Trapped by the weight of its own armored body, it struggles to breathe. If I touch it now, would it still bite me? Why do I have this impulse to soothe what could harm me? I leave it and walk back to the lanai to drink more tea.

From my perch I sense a scurry of movement in the plants. I look left, just with my eyes, head and body still. A mongoose steps out of the shadows, unaware I'm watching. The centipede is dangling from its mouth. Plate after armored plate, the mongoose feeds itself with its little paws, swallowing my great fear whole. I'm reminded that in India mongooses kill snakes.

After it's done, the mongoose scampers along the yard's edge. When it bumps its head on a dangling plant it stops and wrestles the leaves. The plant doesn't wrestle back, but the mongoose doesn't seem to care. For a minute I am privileged to watch a wild animal step out of survival mode and play. I know if I shifted even an inch it would dash into the bushes and I would be left with that sadness that always overtakes me when an animal runs away from me.

I don't think anyone wants to die in the blazing sun. The shade is the place to die: half-light, half-dark. Maybe we would fear it less and not insist so much on the harsh light we call truth that keeps us in denial of how our bodies are just lent to us, not something we possess. They aren't even things, our bodies. They are us. We are them—beyond language, yet the source of it. Everything wants to live.

ODE TO A CENTIPEDE

Thank you for dying at my feet,
for allowing me to carry you
on your final journey
to the mongoose's teeth.

I'm sorry I was so afraid of you.
The next time I will bring you
a bowl of water to drink in the dark
so you don't die thirsty.

All night you stalk roaches
while I sleep and dream
of the day we shake off the dust
and remember the dark
is where light is born.

Bodies spin in womb waters
eyes opening only
when they discover light.

A leader knows her own shadows,
when to fight

and when to surrender.
Praise terror that teaches us
we are only borrowing these bodies.

"I'm descended from the ali'i," my boyfriend told me when we were first getting to know each other under the ironwoods near the beach in Waipi'o. I heard the boast in his voice and wondered if it was true, but to me it didn't matter. I was impressed with *him*—of how he could reach under rocks in the stream and come up with a handful of prawns he made on a fire that took me an hour to build, him ten minutes, and how he always knew where to find fresh water. I didn't care if he was descended from chiefs.

The devil loves to colonize. The boundaries are never clear once they've been violated. He turns people against themselves, especially warriors who no longer have a tribe and place to fight for. He steps in with drugs and alcohol, stokes resentment, and promises to relieve pain that will never be soothed by his spirits.

I saw the devil many times. At first, my innocence kept him away from Waipi'o, he couldn't make it down to the bottom of the valley past my starry eyes. I did encounter him up top when we left the valley to do laundry at his mother's house, watch TV and buy drugs. Hanging out with the devil was pretty normal. The devil here was not that different from the devil back home—only here in Hawai'i he was more out in the open. Back home people snorted lines off mirrors behind closed doors, here people just walked outside to the carport. The devil seemed more normal here, less risky. You could be sitting around the kitchen table at Ronny-Guys' with a bunch of local girls who couldn't stand you while the guys out back snorted coke and watched as the family patriarch sewed the gashed leg of a cock who just won $500 at a fight and have no idea the devil was sitting at the table. Eddie from Kohala could stop by trying to sell some pakalolo. Everyone at the table could sniff a bud, take a hit, say "Neh, no money dis week."

You could walk out back to escape the girls' loathing where Ronny is passing a watermelon around and spitting the seeds on the concrete-covered ground. Kids could be chasing each other around a gutted pig hanging from its feet by the kitchen door. Dogs are barking. Chains clank.

The girls could ask you, "You like eat saimin?" because even if they loathe you, they are polite. You could follow them back into the kitchen and listen to them bicker over who has the worst old man and watch Aunty Lani come home from work and dig her finger into the rice cooker, grind some salt pork and green papaya, then lick her forefinger and thumb. She won't say anything when a Filipino pulls up in a van asking for a half-gram. Nobody really knows him so he drives away empty-handed with only one headlight. Ronny's old lady Robie's, "No shame," trails behind him as he disappears into the night.

Nobody seems to notice it's the devil that makes Robie get up from the table, walk outside and demand a line. Ronny starts griping, "All my money go up your nose!" Robie will smack Ronny one good one.

Tomorrow we go hunt pig in da cane field, neh? someone will say. Ronny makes Milton sweep the concrete yard for a line.

When the devil is present, at 2 AM everyone is wide awake, even Aunty Lani and her old man. The kids are running circles around the hooked pig, the dogs are barking. Chains clank.

Once you let him in, he follows you everywhere, even all the way down to the bottom of a valley. He'll make you cross three rivers and walk a mile up a steep road and somehow get a ride to Honoka'a to score some cocaine.

You can't escape the devil. Whatever he gives you always has to be paid back and the price isn't worth it. He'll take your pride and then your heart. Whatever you love most, that's what he wants. I can guarantee it. I saw it myself when he came for my boyfriend's favorite hunting dog, Kekoa, the one who slept with us and was treated like a pet, not an asset.

Kekoa, whose name meant brave one, was small, but mighty, a legend among dogs, the best pig dog in Hamakua. Of course, the devil wanted him.

Ronny had plenty of dogs, but the devil didn't care about that. The devil wanted my boyfriend on his knees. All those trips back and forth between Waipi'o and Honoka'a pretending he wasn't desperate for cocaine—no money was exchanged.

One day the devil said it was payback time, the way he always does, showing up at the crossroads just when you think you're going to make it to the other side unscathed.

I didn't ask why Kekoa was in the car with us that day on the way to Ronny-Guy's, or even stranger, why he was on a leash. I was shocked when Ronny grabbed him by the neck and dragged him over to a steel peg in the concrete, clipping him to the ground, and even more shocked when my boyfriend said and did nothing. The chain was only a couple of feet.

I couldn't stand up for myself, but I did for Kekoa. I pulled my boyfriend aside and pleaded. I knew I would pay for the humiliation of calling him out in front of his friends.

Kekoa started howling when he turned his back and started to walk toward the car. The devil made me weak. I followed. I watched my boyfriend's eyes roll back in his head like a shark, heart lost in a predator's trance, and knew better than to say a single word about what had just happened. I wanted to stay alive. We never mentioned Kekoa's name again.

At the pond, I have no words. No story rises up to be told. I sit with the silence that isn't really silent at all. I still hear Kekoa howling, and the whining that went on through the long dark hours until the caged roosters, bred to tear each other to pieces, crowed to announce the light was going to return despite our shame.

CHAPTER 16
THE CRACKED MIRROR

⊙

OVERNIGHT, EVERYTHING has changed—two-thirds of the water in the ponds is gone—vaporized. The brain's hemispheres rejoined together so briefly, are again separate, back to their old ways like an old married couple sleeping in twin beds, the gap between them full of shared dreams they can't quite recall when they wake up bleary-eyed and grumbling for coffee.

Imagination exiled from logic. Logic unsupported by imaginative leaps. I know it's probably part of some natural cycle I don't understand, but the ponds *both* look so at-risk, like oil-stained puddles in a bleak industrial city. I'm devastated. What could live in such an inhospitable atmosphere, let alone thrive? The little fish will have a hard enough time, but it seems impossible to me that the King and Queen will have enough water to keep moving. They will be gills up soon, stilled by lack of water, lungs collapsing at air's weight. What lifts the bird, kills the fish out of water.

Because the water is only a couple of inches deep, I can walk over the rock bridge to my old seat, which is exposed now that the water has disappeared. A tiny shrimp flutters out of the stone lean-to where I first saw Crabby. The 'ulili is not here today, just the ghost of its presence flickering in the pond's mirror as the wind moves across it. The Tree of Knowledge and Life are distorted reflections. I don't know what to say.

PELE AND KAMAPUA'A

I wasn't born ugly. I wasn't born bitter. And Pele didn't always rule this island. My people were here many years before she landed, exiled from her homeland. She sailed here in a long canoe with others of her family and found sanctuary. We gave it to her. My people. The people of the fertile, green forests of Hamakua where the waterfalls chant the world into being under the wane and swell of the moon.

I was born in the cool mountains of Ko'olau on Oahu to the goddess Hina. Hina was my mother before she was the goddess of the moon. When she was a young and beautiful girl, she married the man the world calls my father, Olopana, an old man who was no match for her grace and beauty. He was an influential chief, so my mother did her duty in marrying him, but secretly she was in love with his younger brother, Kahiki-ula. Some say he was my father.

Hina would often invite Kahiki-ula to go berry-picking. He always accepted, and wandering the mountain together they talked plant lore and swam in the cool streams. Old, arthritic Olapana was resentful of their friendship but was too proud to say anything. He didn't interfere or ask my mother any questions. Only she knew herself if Kahiki-ula was her lover.

That changed when she gave birth. Olapana refused to acknowledge me as his son. "Let Kahiki-ula claim him," he declared for all to hear, dooming me with his words. "I name this child Kamapua'a. Hog-Child."

I grew up strong and handsome despite his cruel and bitter curse. I was also smart, and some said god-like, since Hina was my mom. Right from the beginning I could shape-shift into all sorts of other creatures from fish to ferns. I thought this would win my father's love or even his approval, but it didn't. The more my father mocked me, the more my hatred for him grew, until I didn't care if he approved of me or not. I left my village and set up a camp in the hills, followed by a few dozen young men who also felt oppressed by my cranky and cruel father. We plundered and pillaged Olapana's lands, devoted outlaws, snorting with laughter as we robbed and killed.

I loved being an outlaw, so I told myself. Loved it so much I shaved my head and tattooed it and my upper body with black, menacing marks. I let a short, bristle grow on my scalp. Hog-Child. Hog-*Man* was more like it. Watch out, Olapana. I even skinned a boar and made a cloak out of its bristly hide. When I looked at my reflection in the stream, even I was horrified. My father wanted a monster, well he'd got one.

They finally caught me. My father himself was going to execute me. My head was on the block. I remember looking up at him as he stood over me with a knife, searching for a glimpse of regret about what he was about to do. None.

One of my father's priests had slipped me a knife. Tired of the old man. Time for a new ruler. If I had seen regret in my father's eyes, even a glimmer of mercy, I wouldn't have plunged the knife into his heart. To be killed while sacrificing his son— not the way my father thought he would leave this world.

I thought I was completely jaded, devoid of innocence or any desire to trust another human being; but I found that after I killed Olapana, the man who was supposed to be my father, I had a desire to know my real father, the one that had birthed me into the world. I went to see Kahiki-ula on Maui, my mother's rumored lover, and asked him if the rumor was true, was he my father. "I do not know you," was all he said. "I have no son."

And that is how I embraced utter debasement: killing, raping, and plundering without mercy, regret, or a shred of shame. I took whatever I wanted in the form of a man or hog. No one could stop me. When I looked in the stream at myself I was no longer horrified.

I had a boat and men to follow me, pirates one and all. One day we found ourselves looking at the shore of Moku o Keawe, and harbored in a lush, green valley between Pololu and Waipi'o. Everybody there was talking about a woman that had recently arrived from across the sea, exiled we heard and moved into Halema'u'ma'u, the crater of Kilauea volcano. They were saying she was the most beautiful—and powerful—woman they had ever seen. The beast in me stirred. I had to have her. My band and I traveled south to find her, and when we did, I fell in love at first sight.

It was dreadful. To fall in love like that. To want something with my whole soul. To be so out of control. I loved her so much I had no shame. I begged her to be my wife. Again and again. She laughed. She mocked me. Just like Olapana. She found my tattoos and head bristle (they call them mohawks now) repulsive. I just wanted to be loved.

I was so crazed with desire and heartache, I decided that if she wouldn't love me I would destroy her. I would rip that mocking laugh right out of her throat, gore her with my tusks, rape her in the mud. I planned my attack.

She was a worthy opponent. I fell on her with the power of rain and storms. She fought back with fire. "If you drown me you'll never have me as a woman," she gasped beneath me.

I was holding her down even though her skin was so hot my hands were smoking. "If you burn me, your own barrenness will starve you," I challenged her back.

I don't know if it was because she wanted me or she was worried her people would starve, but she yielded, and I did, too. In Pele's arms I became soft again. I became the man I'd wanted to be since I was a little child. I felt loved. We were the only people in the world. I looked at her with my eyes full of love and let the monster's mask drop.

It was too much for her. She wanted the monster. She was not ready to be loved.

Pele leaped up from our fern grotto and said the words that doomed us, "No, not again! No! Leave me alone, Kamapua'a. I came here to be queen, not the wife of a king. You are too powerful. You can keep the green valleys of Kohala, Hilo, and Hamakua. I'll stay here in Ka'u and Kona and balance your water with the sun's fire."

She was clearly stuck in her head and not speaking from her heart. I knew if I was patient enough with her, she would meet the water of my emotions and not be overwhelmed. I never wanted to douse her fire.

And then she broke my heart. Pele ran away from my feelings—and from hers. Ignoring my cries for her to stay and talk it out, she fled. "I know you're afraid!" I yelled after her. And then as her silhouette on the horizon became smaller and smaller, "Please come back, Pele! Don't leave me like this! I will die from love!"

My words couldn't catch her. She fled to Kilauea and hid with her family in the caverns beneath the crater. I kept calling for hours, days, years—I don't know how long. I may still be calling in the future. I called so hard the earth shook. This stopped me. It was not me causing the earthquake, Kilauea was erupting. In horror, I realized Pele and her family, hidden in the caverns beneath the volcano, would be incinerated. So would I if I stayed. So I turned and fled toward the water and when I reached the edge plunged in without a thought, transforming into a humuhumunukunukuapua`a, a hog-nosed triggerfish. Even though I could shapeshift, I could never totally escape the monster my father named me.

I swam in my loss for years, never setting foot on shore. Finally I grew tired of swimming and sought sanctuary in the cool, green hills of Kohala, in the river-carved gulches where the maile grows. It was there someone told me Pele and her family had survived, that the fire had actually made them immortal. And I learned that Pele, nine months after I'd leapt in the water, gave birth to our son, Opelu-nui-kauhaalilo, who became the ancestor of many chiefs and common people. People told me Pele, seeing our son, longed for my cooling presence, that maybe I should venture south to see if I could woo her back. I even heard her love chants ringing through the mountains, still do when the wind is right, but I will not venture south to find her. Here in the green forest, I protect the wild pigs who never mock me. Here, soothed by the sound of waterfalls, I protect my wounded heart.

The water is gone. I remember a time when it seemed like it would never stop falling. When it seemed like it had been raining for 40 days and 40 nights, and me an ordinary human unaware she was trapped in a myth, cocooning herself in a yellow wool blanket in a room off the main house Trent built high on stilts from the refuse of the abandoned Peace Corps camp in the days before his wife left him.

I remember hearing him crack open a beer at 4 AM and how he said he was an insomniac when he offered us a bong hit for breakfast. I remember how we were running out of food, which no one but me cared about, and how I contemplated a journey to the papaya tree, but the yard was too muddy. I'd lost the rubber boots lent to me. By that point, I'd lost all my shoes and was used to fording streams barefoot and wading through mud halfway up my shins, but I didn't have it in me. All I could do was go back to bed and curl up in the yellow blanket because it seemed like mine in a world in which everything was mildewing faster than the rain could fall on the tin roof.

My fingers and toes wrinkled like prunes. Under the blanket, the sheets were still dry and I told myself stories of the desert where a cactus blooms once every hundred years just in time for the yearly migration of monarch butterflies to a pine forest high in the mountains of Mexico. And when I ran out of stories, I told myself that afternoon I would find my boots and wade through the mud and pick a papaya. I would make my bed, fold the yellow blanket across the bottom, and walk across the six rivers to the road by the beach that led up and out of the valley. If the road was washed out I would climb Hi'ilawe the waterfall like Rapunzel's braid, and when I reached the top of the tower I'd rest in the familiar beat of my own heart to dream of a valley where rain falls like gold hair growing out of a grave taking over the earth like a nest of cold-blooded vipers. I'd wake up from this nightmare.

I remember Linda's voice calling me to dinner at the trestle table where Trent sat playing along to the Moody Blues on his flute and eyeing the crack pipe volley back and forth like a ball in an innocent game. Everyone seemed too calm to think we were ever going to survive this flood.

Somehow Linda's boyfriend Manny had remembered St. Patrick's Day was coming before the rain started and bought a corned beef. The meat and cabbage were so tender we didn't use forks, laughing at ourselves for being such savages, unlike the English with their high tea, Manny said. *That's the English,* I told them, but they didn't hear me over Manny proclaiming he had Irish blood, even though he *look like one Portagee who nevah seen Hilo.*

Even I been Maui, my boyfriend said, and Linda said she went to New York City one winter, *but it no snow.*

Linda slid a slice of corned beef onto Trent's plate, but he was too intoxicated by the sound of his own flute, and who knows how many beers, to eat. Manny and my boyfriend chewed on chunks of fat glistening in the cabbage, tough and slippery as the snakes banished from Ireland by St. Patrick roughly one thousand years ago, a time when the apocalypse seemed imminent, the wrath of God as real as a snake bite squeezed tight in a tourniquet to stop the poisoned blood from reaching the heart.

I met my boyfriend's eyes and he was telling me I had nowhere left to go, even though he said to everyone else, when they wondered when we'd get out of here, were the flood waters ever going to go down—*Why worry? Dere no snakes in Hawai'i.*

Grind, he told me. *You skinny.* And even though the plate in front of me was full, and I didn't know when we'd get out of there, I'd lost my appetite for fat.

I sat, coiled tight at the table, the rain thundered on the tin roof muffling the sound of the vines smothering the house. Even though I knew I should eat, I'd need my strength, I didn't. I closed my eyes and accepted the facts. I had nowhere else to go.

Trent's flute was a formless trill, a river whose banks had been obliterated. My mind was a dim memory of the sun we hadn't seen in days, maybe even months. Time was an endless forest with no roads creating even an illusion we'd ever get out of it. The guys boasted about how many pig throats they had cut. Linda got up and cleared the table. I clung to the wood edge while she walked across the deck smooth as a serpent, tossing my leftover bones to the pack of cats and dogs scrambling just outside the door.

Here in the Place of Refuge, the water has almost disappeared. I did survive that flood, but a part of me is still there, sitting in dread at the table in the house built from the refuse of the abandoned Peace Corps camp, stomach turning at the congealed fat I can't eat on the plate in front of me. How Manny smacks his lips and shoves corned beef in his mouth with his fingers. How quiet Linda is. My boyfriend is looking across the table at me and I know it's a lie. There are snakes in Hawai'i. I dissolve in the sound of Trent's flute, begging to be spellbound because it's the only way I can think to escape. Freeze.

I might even still be there if someone hadn't forded the rivers far upstream to bring a message to my boyfriend. He was wanted right away up top. While the rain fell on Hamakua, washing away bridges and roads, tearing out torch gingers by the roots, his aunty had been hiding with her three daughters. I never learned why, but I did learn who she was hiding from. Her husband, who, while the rain pushed the ground to the limit to see how much it could endure before collapsing, hanged himself.

As he told it, my boyfriend threw a surfboard into the stream and rode it on his belly almost to the river's mouth, ditching onto shore at the last minute before being swallowed by the ocean's thunder. I don't remember how much time passed until he came back to the house built from the ruins of the abandoned Peace Corps camp and rescued me from under the yellow blanket where I'd been sleeping since he left. And now, after drifting down many other streams, after learning to float, I made it here to this day where I am watching the inhabitants of two little ponds running out of water go on as if they aren't about to die.

CHAPTER 17
TO PENETRATE AN ILLUSION

THIS MORNING when I reach the park I hear the unmistakable trumpet of a pu, a shell horn, ringing through the palms. I walk toward the sound, and when I step off the ramp onto the gravel just past the visitors' center, discover the source. To my left, a young man and woman are chanting in Hawaiian in the woodcarving hale. I recognize the man. We were briefly introduced months ago when I was told he was a descendant of King Kamehameha the Great.

The day I met him he was preparing gourds for ceremony and it's my guess he's the one that works on the carvings in the hale I've passed every day on my way to the ponds. The woman is a park ranger, dressed in a uniform. I stop and wait until they are finished, feeling awkward, but wanting them to somehow know I honor what they're doing. I could probably just say something. She's a park ranger. They both work here, but I can't get the stupid haole tape out of my head and feel like an intruder, so after they're done I shuffle past them as if I've invaded their territory.

At the pond, I discover the water is clear as a two-way

mirror and shallow as a plate of glass. I could break it so easily. Illusions are not always like that. But it's not an illusion. Someone is looking back at me. I feel so close to whoever is on the mirror's other side, I could reach into the mud and pull them into my world where the pressure of having to breathe air in gravity would crush lungs unused to the weight. I let them be. I have learned not to force anything to come to me. No more seeking epic adventure, all I need is contained in this rapidly evaporating water.

The fish are sluggish and I'm worried that the mullet King and Queen won't have enough water to keep swimming. As of now, they're all right, but if the pond loses much more water they'll die. From the rock bridge, I watch them etch infinite loops of transient light like Picasso painting with fire. Unwavering, all muscle and silver scales, they trace their patterns without hesitation until something startles them and they dart away, always coming back to the loop, the endless motion that signifies they're alive. I have no doubt they will continue on until there is no water.

I don't know why my ancestors emigrated from Europe to the American continent, but I imagine it was for the reasons most did, religious freedom and financial opportunity. If they had stories that bonded them to the land, they were lost in the struggle of conquering the American wilderness. None of the European stories were passed down to me, but from my mother's side I was fortunate to hear stories of growing up at the confluence of the Ohio and Muskingum rivers in the legendary town of Marietta, and from my father's side I heard about growing up in the city of Philadelphia as its neighborhoods changed and shifted in the mid-twentieth century, and of summers at the Jersey shore in Stone Harbor where my grandmother fed gulls from her hands on the bulkhead behind the house and my father and his brother got into all sorts of good mischief that has lived on in stories that make that time, for me at least, legendary.

My mother's mother, Dorothy, had a tintype of a Civil War soldier on the dresser in the guest room. It was my fourth Great Grandfather, Gabriel Yates Palmer. She also had a copy of his military records, and I learned that he survived many battles, notably Chattanooga and Antietam, where he was wounded. He survived and made it back to Ohio to marry Jeanette Haddow, who lived into the 20th century. I have a brittle copy of her obituary from the newspaper that says she was a good Christian woman.

Jeannette and Gabriel had a daughter, Mary Eudora, who had a child, Bess, who gave birth to my grandfather Jack Kenney who swam across the Ohio with an inner tube because he had bad lungs. My grandfather could have died swimming across, but he didn't. He also could have died from his lung ailment, which caused a high school teacher to pull my grandmother Dorothy into the hall and tell her not to set her cap for Jack Kenney, but he survived that, too.

My grandmother also did what she wanted. She married Jack who was supposed to be dead and they made my mother Susan who married my father Bruce and they made me.

My fourth great grandfather Gabriel, and all my ancestors going back to the stars, I am the result of your lineage. Though you may have forgotten your stories, I remember them. The grieving is over. I will no longer swim in your unmourned losses, diving down until I think my ears will burst.

Nothing belongs to us, not even our own bodies. What was lost in crossing the Atlantic has come back through my crossing. Here in the Pacific on Moku o Keawe, I proclaim us free.

Time then to be vulnerable. To let these ponds and all the life they hold know how much I love them before it's too late. The water could all be gone tomorrow. Time to let them know I see past my reflection and into theirs to our source.

I take out my notebook, close my eyes, and settle. I become

simple, stop worrying about getting what I want to say just right. Love names, pillow talk, psalms, pour out of my hands as ink on paper. All the colors of the rainbow and then some. I speak the words into the air and listen to the air receive them, sweet secrets we now share. I am unashamed.

When I'm done, I tear the page from my notebook and rest it on the water, words down, first in the left pond, then the right. I give the water time to read my words. After a while, I reach in and retrieve it, slipping a small aquamarine into the water.

As I walk toward the ocean, I'm tearing the sodden page into scraps. They are soggy as something you'd find stuffed in a mouse nest, chittering with life and expectation. Almost at the lava's edge, we find the place we've been searching, a cleft in the rock shelf with direct access to the pounding ocean.

Deep in the cleft, the water is the same aquamarine color as the stone I just offered to the ponds. Waves surge in and out. Just beneath the surface, I see a stone arch carved out by an underwater current that could buttress a cathedral roof. Singing, I let the wet scraps fall from my hands into the crystal blue. Slowly, in no rush, they swirl and begin their downward journey on my wordless song.

What makes a wave? The wind and the moon. I feel the pull of magic drawing me over the lip until I am inside the cleft freeing a scrap caught on the stone ledge. The sound of the waves is muffled by the stone walls but feels louder. As I watch the last scrap sink and swoop between the pillars of the underwater arch, I ask one thing for myself—that the water cleanse my heart of the anxiety that keeps me feeling so unsafe in this world.

The arch is creating a whirlpool that's keeping some of the scraps from sinking. I watch them drift, lulled by the sea sounds into thinking there is no more work to do, that prayers spoken are always heard. This could be true, but even a heard prayer sometimes needs a heart and hands to help it on its way. My love poem is caught between worlds. Hands on my heart, I sing harder.

In the cleft where rock has given way to waves, to the wind and the moon, I sing until my heart has broken 1,001 times in 21 galaxies and the universe says *thank you*, sucking the last scrap through the arch where the ocean finally claims it.

I leave to the sound of drums across Honaunau Bay at Two-Step where the tourists congregate. The two worlds are overlapping.

> Kā' eke to'e a mea
> ite ohn parat'u
> lā me a amā a mā
> kuhi hewa a mā
> a te a mā
>
> To be entangled
> In that which is unnatural
> Now I rise, exposed and brilliant, finally!
> And to penetrate an illusion
> Finally! Finally!

CHAPTER 18
THE KILLING MOON

○

TODAY THE TIDE has pulled even more of the pond's water into the moon. What will the ponds be if they lose all their water? The ponds *are* water. If it's gone, they're not ponds, they're mudholes. Better to refer to things through states of being or verbs, thus shifting names as the elements flow through. Pond becomes "reflecting bowl," and "the overflowing cup where the mongoose drinks," or "ulili's drinking gourd." If the water goes for good, this place can be known as "rest between tears" or "sorrow's waiting room." Each place on Earth, each creature, named this way, is immanent with infinite potential, a locus of possible connections spreading out through words made sacred through the holy attention of particular love.

The night heron has been hunting. His tracks are hieroglyphics, the original alphabet that called us to carve petroglyphs into stone, to paint leaping aurochs and lumbering bears on cave walls. I am blessed by this heron's absence as much as I am by its presence. It has been guiding me all along, probably years before I ever set foot on this island.

The fish are still here but seem muted, oppressed by lack, or they could be totally at peace, the pattern of incoming and outgoing water so deep in their primal consciousness they have no fear of it, their lives defined by rest when the water goes, motion when it comes back. I bet they don't worry at all when the ponds are flush that the tide will pull the water back into the ocean, and when the water goes they are content to rest, because what I perceive as lack gives them time to chill and take a break from the endless motion of survival. Humans make things so complicated. Or at least I do.

I hear 'ulili in the distance, calling out to me from the invisible. Another story for you, wandering tatler. Take it with you when you fly north and tell it to whoever you meet there, tell it as you wing back to the humpback whales swimming back to the Arctic on empty bellies after giving birth in Hawai'i's warm bays. May they carry your song of compassion down. It's needed in the Underworld.

THE WIND FROM HA'ENA

The volcano never let me sleep. When I was young I didn't care so much. I loved the torture of the flames licking the soles of my feet. I loved the way my heat drew men to me. But then I grew older—then old, so old no man would want me. My flame-colored hair was white as ash and I reeked of rotten eggs. I longed for a breeze to blow the stink of myself away.

To my surprise, Ipo-no-eno'e, the Wind from Ha'ena, answered my call and took pity on me. She whispered of a man on Kauai who was waiting for me, a man so beautiful flowers fell at his feet. Lohi'au, a prince of Ha'ena, beating a sharkskin drum all day in the halau, longing for love so much he had scared all the women of his village away.

Ipo-no-eno'e told me I was the only one who could withstand the heat of this young man's yearning. I was intrigued. "But I am old now and ugly," I told the Wind from Ha'ena. "How could he possibly want me?" I knew I could enchant him, but only as a spirit. My body was bound to Kilauea on Hawai'i. What would happen when my magic faded and he saw my true face?

I took the chance anyway.

Leaving my body behind in Hale'ma'uma'u, my home in Kilauea's crater, I traveled to Kauai in my kino wailua, my spirit body, following the sound of a sharkskin drum to the halau in Ha'ena where Lohi'au sat with his friends Mapu and Ka-lei-paoa.

Oh, how I quaked when I saw him. His body was strong and hard as a koa tree, but it was his eyes, fever-bright, that gripped me. He looked insane. Finally, a man who burned the same as me, who would not run and hide in the ocean like Kamapua'a when I got angry. A man who wouldn't fall to pieces and weep. A man who just might consume *me*.

I stepped out of the trees and walked toward the platform where the three men were drumming. In my kino wailua, I was young again. My flame-colored hair swirled to my feet. As I walked toward Lohi'au the crowd jumped back, scorched by my heat. The dancers stopped swaying. One by one the drummers stopped until only Lohi'au played, his drum a living heartbeat. *Ba-boom, ba-boom, ba-boom.*

I didn't stop at the platform. I climbed right up and sat down next to him. *Ba-boom, ba-boom, ba-boom.* His heart, strong as a koa tree. My heart, fierce as the subterranean eruptions that gave birth to our island chain. He had called me across the eight seas that surrounded the Hawaiian Islands from my crater where the sun rises in the East, but when he asked me,

"Where are you from?" I replied, "From here." He knew I was lying because he had searched all of Kauai looking for a lover. There was no way he could have missed me.

"How could I have missed you?" he said and I breathed a sigh of relief that he was going to accept my charade. I would have to tell him someday, but for now, he was willing to dwell in this enchantment with me. I pushed away the thoughts of what would happen when I brought him back to Hale-ma'uma'u and saw my old, withered body and enticed him with my eyes, shooting flames that actually made him blush, but not enough to stop him from rising and descending from the platform when I said, "Let's go somewhere more private."

His friends Mapu and Ka-le-paoa tried to stop him, but he batted them away. I don't think he even heard them. When we got to his hut I couldn't resist letting him kiss me, even though it wasn't real since my body was back in Hale'ma'uma'u. He was so inflamed with desire he couldn't tell he was kissing spirit flesh and not a red-blooded woman who could die like him one day. It did hurt to deceive him, but I pushed that feeling away, too. What did anybody get by feeling guilty? Maybe I would be miserable later, but I was willing to take that risk for this, his hot hands stroking the currents of my body, inflaming the molten streams trying to take form in my spirit flesh. I remembered what it had felt like to be human again, a girl rejected by her own family, fleeing her homeland in a canoe with a few loyal brothers and sisters. I remembered the fear of being trapped in a cave by Kamapua'a who had raped me, then made me love him somehow with his tears.

Kamapua'a's love had made me immortal. If I hadn't rejected him and fled into the caves below Hale'ma'uma'u, I wouldn't have been drowned by lava and become a goddess. I used to secretly thank him for this, but now, my spirit body wrapped in Lohi'au's embrace, just able to feel his touch enough to want so much more, I cursed him. My body had been so lonely.

That is why I let him kiss me, even though I knew it was wrong. I let him lower me onto his mat and begin to untie my pa'u, stopping him over and over again until he was begging. "Please," he moaned in pain, his hand returning to the knotted cloth, but I couldn't let him unravel it and expose my body. In my mind, I felt his pain. In my heart, I felt his pain. And I felt it in my soul, but the body I'd conjured felt nothing. My desire was an act. I had to get him back to Hale-ma-uma'u so I could stop performing. Finally, on the third night, I couldn't stand his suffering any longer and tried to tell him why I wouldn't allow him to take me, but I couldn't get the words out. I didn't tell him it was because my real body was old and ugly, I only told him I needed to go back to Puna to prepare a place for us. "I will send for you in 40 days when it's ready."

Lohi'au did not like this. "I'm ready now!" he raged. I was thrilled, but a little afraid of what I'd started. What would happen with this rage when he found out I'd deceived him? What would he do when he saw my hair was no longer the color of flame? "I must go, Lohi'au. Come to me in Puna after 40 days. If you come I will only ask you to stay five days and five nights. Then you are free to go if that's what you decide."

Lohi'au howled like an animal. "Don't you understand I love you! I want to stay with you forever!" Now I was more than a little afraid. Maybe he did love me, but I wouldn't be sure until he had seen my true face.

"I'm going." I walked toward the hut door. He ran and blocked my way. "I won't let you leave!" I tried to slip past him, but he grabbed my arm and twisted it behind my back. The pain was heart-wrenching. It didn't hurt my body because it couldn't feel, but I was disgusted with myself that I'd pushed him to this. I looked into his eyes to see if I could reach him, but all I could see was my own reflection in his black pupils. He snarled at me. I didn't know what to do. How could I leave him like this, twisted and insane?

But I had to go back if we had any hope of being together. I snarled back and bit his hand to free myself. He held on until I broke the skin and then I ran for the trees. By the time he reached the grove I was gone, a puff of smoke lifted by Ipo-no'ene'e, the Wind from Haena who carried me back to my home in the East.

I sent my younger sister Hi'iaka to bring him to me. She had been keeping vigil over my body in Hale'ma'uma'u all this time, worried because the earth below us had not stirred in days. Everyone else thought I was in a deep sleep, but she suspected I had traveled somewhere in my kino wailua and had wandered to the land of the dead ruled by the goddess Milu. I awoke to the sound of her chanting and told her how I'd fallen in love with the most beautiful man on Kauai. She agreed to go get him for me, asking only that I protect her dear friend Hopoe, who she cherished so much she'd gifted her an ohia lehua forest where the two of them would rest and play watching the i'iwi drink nectar from the spiny red blossoms of the sacred trees. I promised to guard Hopoe and the beautiful forest where my sister and her friend passed so many sweet days. "Just bring him back to me," I pleaded. Her two friends Wahine, a human woman, and Pa'u'o'pala'e agreed to accompany her.

There are many tales of Hi'iaka's adventures on the way to Kauai to bring Lohi'au back. It's true she was a fierce and wily warrior, as well as beautiful. She was my sister. People still tell those stories today, of how she conquered monsters, and even the evil mo'o people as she traversed the slippery gulches of the mystical vallies—Waipi'o, Waimanu, Pololu, places where stories rose up from springs that flowed into streams that flowed into rivers meeting the sea, where the shark god Kamo-hoali'i patrolled the reef's edge, picking off the weak to keep the balance between predator and prey. Many places in those valleys are named for her triumphs, and many still speak of her exploits on Maui, Molokai, and Oahu, and they have certainly not forgotten what she and Wahine did (the only companion left by the time they arrived on Kauai) when they reached Ha'ena and discovered it was too late for her to bring Lohi'au back to me. They had done their best, but with all those famous exploits people admire, they arrived after the 40 days I'd told Lohi'au to wait.

After I'd left, Lohi'au had hung a kapu sign on his hut. "Keep out." His friends Ka-lei-papa and Ka-hua-nui tried to reach him, but he ignored their pleas. His weeping was so terrible they were ashamed for him. They kept everyone away.

How many days past 40 did this man wait for me, noble and strong as a koa tree? Did he beat his sharkskin drum until the only thing he could hear was his own heart pounding through his blood to get to me?

The weeping finally stopped. Ka-lei-papa and Ka-hua-nui thought he would come out of his hut and join them on the beach, maybe go for a surf, but he didn't appear. The silence grew so heavy and ominous, the two friends ignored the kapu sign and entered his hut.

Lohi'au was dead. He had hanged himself with his own malo.

Hi'iaka and Wahine discovered his body high up in a cave, transported by two sorceresses he had rejected. The sorceresses had also been enchanted with him and were offended he'd rejected their advances. Now they were having their way with his dead body, keeping it warm with their deviant spells.

Everybody loves the story of how Hi'iaka and Wahine defeated the sorceresses, how they summoned Maui to hold back the sun to give them enough time to reach the cave before dark and battled the witches with magical pyrotechnics that attracted the wandering spirit of Lohi'au to the cave where his dead body was being showered with gruesome caresses and fireworks, of how Hi'iaka realized that the sorceresses were going to destroy Lohi'au's soul so that it could never be reunited with his body, how at the last possible second my sister destroyed the witches with a final burst of energy and ensnared Lohiau's soul. Everybody's heard of how my sister Hi'iaka-i-ka-wai-ola sprinkled the water of life from her calabash onto his corpse, and how the people below danced and chanted, channeling mana from the gods to help her. How they loved her, Wahine holding Lohiau's ankles and Hi'iaka maneuvering his captured soul back into his body through his eyes—yes, it was painful—excruciating in fact, the slow descent of soul inch by inch back into his body. It was like pushing a fish hook back through your palm after you've snagged yourself, the barb gouging out new pathways of pain before the original wound had healed. Everyone knows how Laka and Lono were so impressed with Hi'iaka that they sent their own personal rainbow to the cave to save them the long climb down. Yes, it was a marvel how Hi'iaka, Wahine, and Lohi'au descended on a rainbow. Yes, Hi'iaka deserved the crowd's adulation and elation that Lohi'au was alive again. She was the one there, not me, who watched his jubilation as he came back into his body and ran into the sea to surf a multicolored wave, roiling again with energy and life.

I wish I had been brave enough to let him see my withered, old body instead of pushing his hands away those three days and nights he'd burned to possess me. I wish I had given him the choice. In a way it was my fault what happened next. *No*, it *was* my fault. I'll say it, just this once and you'd better forget it because I don't take well to being reprimanded and you don't want to be the one to pay.

Hi'iaka and Wahine set forth from Ha'ena, journeying back through the islands, bringing my Lohi'au. They had a lot more adventures, turning shark gods into men, you know the way it goes with demigoddesses, they like to show off to mortals because they know half of them are as vulnerable and weak as they are. Finally, they reached Hawai'i Island, long past the 40-day deadline.

I believe promises must be kept. Hi'iaka had *promised* me she'd be back with him in 40 days. If she hadn't been so eager to be a heroine she could have done it. She wanted the glory. She could have made it in forty days.

I'm sure she was attracted to Lohi'au right away. Who wouldn't have been? He was the most beautiful man in the Hawaiian Islands, but I don't think she would have done what she did next if I hadn't destroyed her friend Hopoe and their beautiful ohia lehua forest. It was my act that led *her* to act on her desire for my true love, and she planned it to be as devastating for me as she probably was when she heard I'd killed Hopoe. She fucked him right at the base of Kilauea in full sight of people, no shame or attempt to hide in the ferns. I ordered her friends Pa'u'o'pala'e and Wahine to kill Lohi'au, but they wouldn't do it. For that, I blasted them off the earth.

When I reached the faithless lovers at the base of Kilauea they were covered in dust and ash, a feeble attempt by lackeys to appease me. I was not amused. There they were, basking in the afterglow of their rutting. I had never felt more betrayed or humiliated. When Lohi'au saw me he jumped up and yelled, "This is between you and your sister. Leave me out of it!" Weasel. "You will not escape my vengeance!" I raged at him. I released wave after wave of lava and that took care of that bitch-boy. Buried under lava. What a way to go. Now it was time to ruin Hi'iaka. But she had always been wily and once again slipped past me, burrowing underground to hide and bide her time until she could bring Lohi'au back to life again. Down she went, into the land of Milu, the underworld. Her plan was not only to revive Lohi'au, but to carve a tunnel that would allow the waters of Milu to rush to the surface. She knew the collision of underworld water with my lava could destroy me and quite possibly the entire world.

Hi'iaka blasted through the first two levels of Milu, but on the third level, she encountered the suicide god, eternally hanging from a noose, with bulging eyes and tongue hanging out of his mouth. The sight was so grotesque she almost failed, but she pushed on through her terror to the fourth level where she found her friends that I had killed, Wahine and Pa'u'o'pala'e. Ever the generous one, she restored them to life and as they ascended she kept going down to Milu's lowest level where the underworld river hissed like a serpent waiting for someone to channel its deadly fury.

Wahine and Pa'u'o'pala'e arrived up top just in time to find me about to decimate a man groveling before me. He was weeping so hard his face was covered in snot. "Pao'a!" they cried. When I heard his name I realized the man before me was Lohiau's best friend. His grief had brought him to the foot of Kilauea where he was determined to speak his truth before dying because of course, he knew I was going to kill him. If it hadn't been for those two girls bursting up from Milu I would have. Instead, I heard this: "He hanged himself out of grief for you, Pele!"

Even though I've been telling you the story of how Lohi'au hanged himself, and of how Hi'iaka brought him back to life to bring him back to me, at the time Pao'a wept before me, I didn't know it. I thought my lover and sister had betrayed me. I also didn't know Hi'iaka had resisted her attraction to Lohi'au the entire journey until she'd heard I had killed Hopoe and burned her beloved forest.

All's fair in love and war.

Who said that? I don't recognize the accent. Some god from another dimension? I decide the rules here. Still, there was some truth in it. Guilt began to creep in. Regret. Memories of sailing with my sister on the canoe that brought us to Hawai'i, banished from our homeland. Combing each other's hair. Laughing at our reflections in forest pools and wondering who our lovers would be.

It was a long way down, the most difficult journey of Hi'iaka's life. Finally, she reached the bottom and beheld the River of the Dead. Her eyes were slits of silver fire compared to my gold. She raised her hands to summon the power of Milu's waters to release destruction on the world above.

I have no idea why, but our father Kane stepped in. None of my siblings and I had heard from him in a while. He was a distant father and never seemed to care much about any of us. He rarely left Hunamoku, his floating island in the clouds. Before Hi'iaka could summon the power of the River of Milu, our absentee father stopped her. "You don't belong here, Hi'iaka. You still belong to life. You must go back." My sister probably knew it was no use resisting him and gave up her quest for vengeance. She's never told me, but I imagine it was a bitter journey back through the Underworld to the surface where I was still Queen, and I'm sure she probably expected to be killed as soon as she surfaced.

You know what she heard on the way up? A love song.

You know who was singing? Lohi'au.

Lohi'au, the man I loved, was singing, not to me, but to my sister Hi'iaka. I should have been even more enraged with jealousy, but something inside of me started to thump and quake. It was my heart. I waited for it to explode and unleash the fire that was me, but no matter how many outrageous scenes of betrayal I replayed in my mind, the lava stayed inside the earth, swirling beneath my feet, but coming no closer to the surface. I heard a hissing sound, water and fire coming together. Could it be my tears striking the lava? I will not be the one to say.

So that's how it ended. When I heard Paoa's revelations

of how much Lohi'au had grieved me, and of how Hi'iaka had resisted her feelings for Lohi'au until I'd destroyed her best friend and the place she loved most, my heart softened. I know people probably don't think I have a heart, but I do. Everyone does. We are all held in the heart of the gods beyond the gods, the great mystery we pass through as it passes through us, changing shape like earth shaped by wind and water, never recognizable but always so familiar. The only way to come close to understanding it is to close your eyes and listen to the *ba-boom, ba-boom, ba-boom* inside you, your own heart that once rested close to your mother's rib cage.

The heart is not caged within bones. If you listen with the ears of an embryonic bird still nestled in an egg, or the ears of a whale encased inside a double-layer of water, womb, and the vast ocean in all directions, you'll hear it moving through everything created and uncreated, visible and invisible. There is a word for it: aloha mā. Self-reflective love. In la kech a la kin, say the Maya. *I am another you.* It's difficult to understand with the mind, but the heart knows.

I wouldn't bring Lohi'au back to life—my newly softened heart was too tender—but I allowed Kanemilo to do it. For the second time, Lohi'au's body was reunited with his soul. I gave them my permission to marry, but I couldn't bear to have them live so close. I told Hi'iaka if they wanted to be together they had to go to Kauai. If they left I wouldn't harm them. I even managed to save some face by taking Pao'a as a lover for three days. He didn't seem to notice I was old and ugly. Maybe I wasn't anymore.

Hi'iaka and Lohi'au remained together, happy, until his mortal life came to an end. She did not revive him a third time. Because of all her adventures and brave deeds on her journey to Kauai and back again, she has since been revered as the goddess of pathways and wanderers. Sometimes you can still hear lost travelers pray to her. Does she answer? Let me know. I am still here, awake and fiery-eyed in Halema'uma'u crater. Don't come too close. Or do. If I destroy you, it's only because I love you.

Leave it to me to deny Pele the last word. No further comments. I've been warned before. This time I'm listening.

CHAPTER 19
AND I SAY, IT'S ALRIGHT

◉

I GET TO THE PARK just before sundown, No one's around—at least no one human. The ponds are half-empty. There's no denying it with positive thinking—they aren't even close to half-full. How can the King and Queen possibly survive in such shallow water? But one of them flashes close to me, a brush with lightning, then loops to the pond's far side.

Auku'u's tracks are still here, which means the water has not risen high enough to wash them away all those hours the sun blazed down on this little world I've come to love. I sit down between the two ponds on the rock bridge and face left, regard the tattered Tree of Knowledge and the shorter Tree of Life to its right, thriving just fine in the wall's shadow.

Tonight I find I don't have much to say about myself. I can't even remember what all the fuss was about. What am I doing here? I may as well tell a story.

THE PURSUIT OF DERMOT AND GRAINNE

I suppose this all began that day when Roc's son was frightened by an animal and ran between Donn's legs to hide. Nobody knows why, but Donn, who could have helped the lad, instead squeezed his legs together until there was no air left in the boy. His heart stopped. He was dead.

Roc was enraged, rightfully so, he was quite mad in his grief, mad enough to perform a magical ceremony that brought his son back to life. But not as a human boy. Roc put his son's spirit into the body of a wild boar. He also put a geis on the boar-boy to kill Donn's son, who himself had a geis put on him never to pierce the skin of a pig. If you're confused, don't worry too much about the details. Just listen and soon enough it will all play out the way it's supposed to for *you*. There's something for all of us in a story like this, something ancient as a bear skull in a den that can only be reached by descending deep inside a cave whose opening is a slit just big enough for everyone who needs to squeeze through it.

Now a geis was a strange, contradictory thing, combination curse, spell, taboo, and obligation, that could also be a blessing. These were not just things that existed in ancient Ireland, most of us are still under a geis today and probably will be in the future, if we have one, for we need them. A geis is not necessarily a bad thing. Sometimes the limits of an obligation are the only thing that can evolve us.

You may have heard of Donn's son. Dermot O'Duibhne was his name. He was the boy I mentioned at the beginning of this jaunt, the boy with a geis on him never to kill a pig, cursed by Roc who had lost his own son to the cruel act of Dermot's father. Despite the curse, Dermot was the greatest warrior of the Fianna, the band of roving warriors led by Finn MacCool, who we met earlier as a young boy sucking on his thumb after mistakenly burning it on the Salmon of Knowledge, whose wisdom had seeped into him that fateful day by the River Boyne.

Some of you may even know that Dermot was also known as Dermot of the Love Spot. Bol Sherca it was called in Gaelic, a mark that made anyone who saw it fall in love with him, a permanent Cupid's arrow smack in the middle of his forehead. Dermot did his best to keep the Love Spot covered, growing long bangs through which he looked up, tilting his head in a way that made the court ladies swoon thinking he was a flirt, but he was not tempted by them. His loyalty was to Finn Mac-Cool and the Fianna.

At the time of our story, Finn MacCool was getting on in years. He could still leap across the great chasm he tested himself against every year on his birthday, but he could foresee a day soon when he wouldn't quite make it and would have to pull himself up in an undignified scramble. That would be the day to surrender his leadership of the Fianna. In the meantime, he resolved to enjoy life to the fullest—the feasting, the fights, the poetry and sharing of song and story, the pleasures of the marriage bed—only Finn didn't have a wife. The mother of his son Ossian had been a deer woman and had slipped away into the forest shadows many years ago. Finn was a great king, but a lonely man. He needed a wife.

He consulted with the Fianna who all agreed, the only woman in Ireland worthy of being his wife was the daughter of the High King Cormac Mac Airt. Grainne was her name, and she was known as a woman whose intelligence equaled her beauty. They sent some men to the High King's court and asked for Grainne's hand. Would she marry the greatest leader the Fianna had ever known, poet-warrior Finn MacCool, whose hands carried magical healing powers, who could charm the birds in the trees and never lost a game of chess to anyone but his most trusted warrior, Dermot?

If only they had sent Dermot to offer for her hand, things

would have been much different, for unbeknownst to the Fianna, Grainne had glimpsed him as a twelve-year-old maid on the hurling field. The wind had blown back his hair and she saw it full-on, the Bol Sherca, the Love Spot. She was slayed, bound to him in an instant. Poor Dermot had no idea.

If only… two little words that keep so much from surrendering to the completion of grief. We are going to erase them now, gently like water straying from the river at the bend, splashing a little further up the sandbank than usual before rejoining the story, the river on its way to the sea. No regrets. It's time to truly grieve and release ourselves from the hungry ghosts that blight our future.

Anyway, Grainne had been waiting for this boy for a long time—all through her girlhood. Although a young maiden, she was already a bit disillusioned with love. The boy with the Love Spot had not come. When would he come? Maybe he wasn't coming. He wasn't coming. She lost faith. So it was, "Yes, I'll marry him," when the Fianna came courting for the old chief Finn MacCool.

She left her father's house and journeyed to the hall of the Fianna, and it was there, peering from behind a curtain as she was about to enter the feast, that she had her first doubts; first when she spied her intended's son, Ossian, so handsome with the elegant shine of the deer passed onto him from his mother. Finn, sitting next to him, though handsome and clearly a man of dignity, was weathered. Deep lines on his forehead and cheeks. Just a few gray hairs, but still, he was no Ossian. And he was certainly no Dermot of the Love Spot, who Grainne spied next, recognizing in an instant the youth she'd fallen in love with at 12-years-old. She knew immediately she could not marry Finn MacCool.

As I said, Grainne was a woman whose intelligence equaled her beauty, She stepped from behind the curtain and took her place next to Finn. She smiled and nodded and nobody had any idea what was going on inside her, how she wanted to leap with all her being into the arms of her future husband's most trusted warrior. No one had any idea how hard it was to keep her hands and voice from shaking as a servant she'd commandeered poured wine containing a sleeping potion in everyone's goblet except for hers and the leaders of the Fianna. Boom. Heads dropped on the table. Snores. Most undignified. The Fianna looked at her in shock. She was steady-eyed, asking each one of them if they would run away with her. "I can't marry him," she told them without guilt or shame. No need for explanation. It was what it was. Absolutely loyal to their chief Finn MacCool, every one of them refused. Finally, she came to her real target, Dermot of the Love Spot.

"And you Dermot? Will you run away with me?" she asked him directly.

"My lady, with all due respect, my loyalty belongs to Finn MacCool, my great chief."

Grainne had no choice—remember, she had been bound to him years ago because of his Love Spot, though she didn't reveal that to him. "Well, then," she said. "I place a geis on you. You are bound to run away with me."

Dermot's heart sank, knowing he was going to have to tear his heart in two, leaving half with Finn and taking the other half into the wilds with this woman. No one could disobey a geis. It wasn't just unheard of, it wasn't possible. Some things in life just are. He had no choice.

And so Dermot set off with Grainne while Finn was still asleep. Grainne was not used to hard travel and whined in a most un-royal way, demanding Dermot carry her. He refused hoping she would give up and go back to Finn and this could all be over. The drama of their situation had attracted Aengus Og, the god of love, who thoroughly approved of their match. He gave them some advice: they were never to sleep in a cave with one opening, or a house with one door, or a tree with one branch, and they would never be able to eat where they cooked or sleep where they ate. Band on the run. They would have to keep moving if they wanted to keep ahead of Finn and the Fianna, for everything Dermot feared was true.

The next morning when Finn awoke at the banquet table to find them gone, his heart broke, not so much at the loss of Grainne—that sting was pride's—but from his friend's perceived betrayal. Dermot knew he was loyal, but Finn had no idea he had only fled with Grainne because she'd placed him under geis. He gathered the Fianna and set off in pursuit, intent on revenge.

With Finn in hot pursuit, Dermot and Grainne fled across the land. Each night Dermot would make a nest somewhere for them to sleep, but he never touched Grainne. He remained chaste. He would leave a piece of raw fish in each place they slept as a sign to Finn that he had not touched his intended, which only enraged Finn more.

Closer and closer they came. Sometimes Dermot and Grainne could actually hear the hounds of the Fianna. It was on one of those days that, when fording a stream, water splashed up Grainne's thigh. Cool and delicious, ticklish was the water. She flushed. She quite liked the feeling. Looking up at Dermot, also flushed, standing on the riverbank offering her his hand while trying to look away, she said, "That water has more courage than you."

I don't know if it was because he truly wanted her or if it was the shame of being called less than a man, but Dermot took Grainne to bed that night, bedding down in a nest of crushed grass and ferns like the forest deer. Now they were husband and wife. He left no messages of purity after that for Finn.

One night they disregarded the advice of Aengus Og and slept in a house with seven doors. Wouldn't you know it, the Fianna finally caught up with them and blocked each door. No escape.

Aengus Og descended saying he would spirit them to safety, but Dermot refused. He had been ready for this to be over since the beginning. No, he would battle it out, fight his brothers and his chief. "Go with Aengus Og," he growled at Grainne, who let the love god spirit her away.

Dermot began opening doors. One by one, six doors opened, each one of his brothers offered him the chance to escape. Dermot closed each door until he came to the seventh and there, face to face at last, was his best friend, the chief to whom he'd sworn fealty, the great Finn MacCool. "You're a dead man if you come out that door Dermot O Duibhne," roared his chief.

Dermot stepped through and the wrath of Finn and the Fianna were on him. Swords clashed, spears clanked, hounds bellowed. Dermot was everywhere at once. No one could strike a fatal blow, the battle went on and on until Dermot, taunting the Fianna, ended it in one leap off the tip of his spear—up and over the warriors he sprang, fleeing to Grainne who was safe in the company of Aengus Og.

This time he built a proper camp for them. He had lost his band of brothers, betrayed and broke his best friend's heart; maybe it was time to enjoy what little life he had left in him.

There was a famous rowan tree in the forest. Dubhros was its name, and this tree was said to have sprouted from a berry dropped by one of the Tuatha De Danaan, the fairy folk. Anyone who had three berries from it would be restored to health. The berries could heal all wounds, even make a middle-aged body young again. The tree was guarded by a giant, Searbhann Lochlann who could only be defeated by three strokes of his own club.

It just so happened there were three warriors who lived near that place who'd been at odds for a long time with Finn Mac-Cool. When they heard he was nearby they approached him and asked to make peace. Finn looked at the three and saw an opportunity. "I'll make peace with you if you bring me the head of Dermot or three berries from Dubhros, The Rowan Tree."

He was tired from this long chase. The men saw it. Still, they knew he was strong enough to slay them all with one sword and that if they wanted peace, they'd have to choose one of the options. Dermot was known far and wide as undefeatable. The berries were guarded by a giant. Their prospects were not good. "Let's give it a go," they said to each other. They might all be dead by the end of the day, but they were tired of fighting. One last try, then.

Early one morning they snuck into Dermot and Grainne's camp. Dermot heard the rather dim barbarians rustling in the brush. After bashing their heads together, he trussed them up and laid them in a heap at Grainne's feet. Unable to move, the three warriors quickly confessed what they were about, "We only wanted to make peace with Finn MacCool," they blabbered. "He told us our options were to bring him your head or three berries from the sacred rowan tree that restores youth and beauty."

Grainne's ears pricked up at that. Perfect health? Luminous beauty? Yes, please! All these years on the road had taken their toll on her complexion and lately, her bones had begun to ache. "Dermot, my love, bring me those berries." She was a woman good at asking for what she wanted.

When Dermot didn't look eager to leap into battle with a giant, she tried another approach, "My bull, my big, strong-shouldered man, I could use those berries. I haven't told you yet because I've been waiting for the right moment, but I think I'm with child."

Dermot had no choice. Grainne was to bear him a child. Tired of fighting and fleeing, heavy-hearted, he set off to battle the giant Lochlann, guardian of the sacred rowan tree, to please his expectant wife. This time he was not able to leap over the giant on the tip of a spear. It was a bloody, bashing battle between the two of them that almost got the best of Dermot. Finally, blinded by his own blood, Dermot got his hands on the Giant Lochlann's club and bashed him over the head three times with it, cleaving his skull from fontanelle to the base of his neck. The giant's brains spilled onto the soil of Erin.

Dermot was not proud of it, he took no joy in killing a fae guardian. He hadn't even felt blood lust, only resignation. It was what it was. He picked some berries for Grainne, then some more for the three warriors to take back to Finn. "Maybe some unforeseen good will come from this," he thought. Grainne was delighted with the berries. She did look even more beautiful, Dermot noticed. Why not take up residence in this leafy fountain of youth? He built them a little treehouse up in the branches and they moved in with the birds.

Now there's something you should know about our fated, fleeing lovers. In all their years of wandering, wherever they spent the night curled in each others' arms, the soil grew richer and more fertile, fields burst with barley and wheat, enough to make it through the winter and more. Wives were more fertile and husbands more virile. Stories began to be told that the love of these two blessed the land. The verb of their loving became a noun, a healing balm. Poems were written about them. People left little offerings at springs and in apple orchards in their names. Finn heard this as he followed them, and his heart grew even more bitter. Once the people praised him, now he was the cuckold chief, chasing a woman he barely knew and didn't love out of pride. The three warriors were right, life force was draining out of him. He was starting to look like a hollowed-out lightning tree.

When the three enemy warriors gave him the berries, he smelled Dermot on them, the musky sweat of his most trusted friend. He knew the warriors were lying when they said how they'd got the berries, but now he also knew where Dermot and Grainne were hiding, so he let their deception slide. He gathered the Fianna, a ragtag bunch soured by their leader's bitterness at this point, and they shuffled into the forest to find this holy rowan.

Now Finn was known to love a good game of chess. When they found the tree, he challenged his son Ossian to a game. Ossian was a good player, but rather like Telemachus, he was no match for his father. Three times Finn had Ossian trapped, three times his son surprised him by countering his moves that kept him in the game. Funny thing, each time Ossian countered, a berry from the rowan fell onto the square, guiding Ossian to victory. Finn leaped to his feet, spilling the chess board. He knew there was no way Ossian could beat him. The only man who could beat the great Finn MacCool, bearer of the Salmon of Knowledge's wisdom, was Dermot O'Duibhne. "Are you up there, Dermot?" he hollered into the branches.

"I am!" Dermot replied without hesitation. Fuck it. "And with Grainne, too!" The leaves parted and there they were, Dermot and Grainne in passionate embrace, kissing so hard their teeth clashed and berries burst their skins, spraying the Fianna with dark juice. "Come down," Finn demanded. "Finish this as a man and not a bird hiding in a tree. Come face me at last. Fight your chief."

Dermot heard this and something inside him broke, some thread of loyalty to the past that had nothing to do with the man who had suffered for so many years as an exile, not by choice. Could not Finn have listened? Could he not have understood his beloved Dermot was under a geis? Could he not have asked, Dermot, why have you done this? Even now he was waiting for Finn to say, "Come down from that tree and let's talk like brothers," but it didn't happen. Instead, he heard his chief turn to the Fianna and say, "If you let him leave here alive I will kill each one of you. Whoever kills him I will grant the highest honor. Songs will be written in your name."

This was too much for Dermot. Words burst out of him like

fire-tipped arrows. "I am a fugitive because of you, living a half-life. Now you would kill me! Really? After all I've done for you? Now you would turn everyone against me, my own brothers the Fianna. I will never fight for you again, Finn MacCool, but I will fight for myself!" And with those words, he jumped out of the tree into the midst of the Fianna swinging his sword and screaming like a banshee.

Only it was not Dermot. It was Aengus Og in his shape, which Finn realized after the Fianna had decapitated him several times only to have his head grow back right in front of their eyes. The real Dermot had escaped on one of his dolphin leaps, spinning and whirling high above the fracas.

The Fianna were too weighed down by bitterness to follow him. Soon Dermot was far from the lovers' tree, landing at Grainne's feet who Aengus Og had once again spirited away to safety. He looked up at her and finally, was truly enchanted by her ravishing beauty. "Not a bad fate," he smiled up at her. She gave him a Mona Lisa smile that promised secret delights. At last, Dermot accepted her.

They resumed their flight, but this time enjoyed it more, especially the nights when they lay down in their nests of bracken under the white Milky Way surrounded by snorting deer who danced with them in their shared dreams. Finn kept on with his pursuit, turning to his skills as a diviner as his body aged. All three of them were exhausted, but didn't know what else to do but go on. One day fate would find them all and end the story for them. In the meantime, there were days of walking and nights of legendary lovemaking. Grainne sang to Dermot when he was tired, soothing him with lullabies she learned from the moon. Sometimes he woke in a cold sweat, brandishing his sword at the dark night, convinced the Fianna were upon them. Those were the times their lovemaking was the sweetest. When Dermot smelled the honey hair of Grainne, felt her skin smooth as river pebbles bumping up against his flinty bones when he sank into her silence, he was overcome with so much gratitude at the world's beauty he wept. Grainne would smooth his hair from his forehead as he rested on top of her, careful not to crush her, though she'd just been urging him to do just that, the imprint of rocks on her spine, her hips sparking like silica.

One day they were sheltering in a cave by the sea when the waves brought an ocean being to shore, Ciach, The Fierce One, who had traveled there over the western sea in his seal-skin coracle. Ciach was a chess player and gladly accepted Dermot's challenge. Ciach's ocean magic outwitted Dermot's more steady land wisdom, and the sea being won the match. Under the sway of this ocean man, Dermot was not himself. He casually mentioned that perhaps Ciach could claim Grainne as the prize for winning.

Shocking, right? Well, I will have to say I heard Grainne was not entirely enraged by this. After years of being chased, she loved the drama of a good fight and the potential of a new lover, but she pretended she was indignant and laid into Dermot, and pretty soon the heat of her words and his retorts had inflamed her. As Criach disappeared from the tawdry scene she grabbed a knife and plunged the blade into Dermot's thigh.

Dermot did not scream in pain. Grainne did not beg for forgiveness. Instead, they looked at each other for a long time, as long as it took for white flowers to blossom from rowan branch tips, for those flowers to harden into berry buds, for those berries to ripen and fall to earth a thousand times. It was a silence there was no coming back from. A numb silence. Finally, Dermot spoke.

"You took everything from me. My people. The freedom of walking under the sun. I am hunted like an animal by the ones I loved. I have no honor. My life is a joke. You have made me your jester, here to entertain you and satisfy your every whim. I have killed a giant for you who only wanted to guard a sacred tree. I am defiled and so are you. If only you could have loved Finn MacCool, the finest man I ever knew. If only you would hate me."

Grainne finally heard the truth. I mean really heard it. It flooded her like an un-dammed stream and the pain was so great she had a hard time breathing. Words—sounds really—sputtered out of her like a half-strangled rabbit. "I'm sorry," she gasped.

"My love, I couldn't help it. When I saw you as a 12-year-old girl—when I glimpsed the Love Spot, I was lost from that moment. No man besides you would ever do for me. I drowned in your beauty and I've been kicking to the surface to breathe ever since. I couldn't help it. Dermot, you are all I have. You are my stag on the mountain. You are my *mountain*. I beg you, don't leave me."

Dermot looked at her on her knees before him and began to speak. I'll not tell you what he said, only that it went on for a long time. Back and forth they accused and forgave until finally they were all talked out and sat together on a blanket of quiet.

"Are you hungry, Dermot?" Grainne asked. He nodded yes. "Then hand me the knife so I can cut this bread I baked for us before all this drama."

"My love, the knife?" Grainne asked again after Dermot did not reply. Finally, she stopped and looked at him and the look in his eyes took whatever she was about to say next right from her lips.

"Look for the knife in the sheath," Dermot said, without accusation, utterly defeated by all he'd lost in the name of a love he'd never wanted.

All this time she'd forgotten the knife was still stuck in his thigh. For the rest of her life she would know no deeper shame.

Finally, after sixteen years everyone grew tired of this endless, futile pursuit. Dermot and Grainne would stop fleeing. Let

Finn have his revenge. He had earned it. But once again Aengus Og intervened, persuading Finn not to punish the lovers. Finn offered his terms. He would give up his pursuit if they would live quietly in Sligo, not rubbing their love in his face at court. The lovers agreed and settled down to make a life together. Ireland wept with relief. Finn returned to court with the Fianna. Dermot and Grainne settled into married life, coming to know each other in a different way, through the day-to-day tasks of tending the land and raising a family. Nobody was chasing them. Life was not exciting, but there were other rewards, and they still enjoyed the comfort of each other's bodies under goose down on long winter nights.

But there was something about the vagabond life that Grainne had not reckoned on. After years of being chased, she found she missed the drama. She may even have become addicted to it. Sometimes she found herself picking fights with Dermot for no reason or screaming at her kids for laughing too much. You've seen it before, making mountains out of molehills. That's what happens when adrenaline becomes a god.

One night sitting by the fire with Dermot she said, "Husband, don't you just wish for some excitement around here?" Dermot looked around. He had grown used to the domestic comforts. "I hadn't thought of that," he said tentatively. He had known Grainne long enough to know when he should pay attention. What was she up to? Was she going to turn his world upside down again?

What she said didn't seem so drastic at first. "We have everything we've ever wanted, my dear, thanks to you and all you suffered, but I can feel there's still a hole in your heart. I'd like to heal that wound by inviting Finn MacCool and the Fianna to a feast here in our hall. Wouldn't it be grand to feast once again with the Fianna?"

This was not what Dermot expected, but when he heard the words he realized it *was* what he wanted most in the world.

Grainne, that witchy enchantress, had seen right into his soul. Mesmerized at the thought of reuniting with his beloved chief and band of brothers, he answered her as if under a spell, convincing himself this was a marvelous idea. "Yes, it would. The best feast I can imagine would be one with Finn and the Fianna at my table once again. To sit with them and sing until dawn! I can imagine nothing I'd like more. Grainne, you're right. But do you think they'd come?"

Grainne did think they'd come, for she knew these warriors were even more hooked on the drama than she was, they had all been calibrated by blood lust, their nervous systems thrummed to ax and drum. She could hear their hearts pounding under their skin from miles away, these men who had fought over her, and knew they would never be satisfied until the tension had burst. "I do," she told Dermot, and the words were like a marriage vow.

The invitation was sent. Finn and the Fianna accepted. They would come in a year to feast at the table of Dermot and Grainne. Preparations began immediately. The villagers, people who had gathered around the exiled lovers, were happy to do the work. It was all they could talk about for the whole year, how Finn and the Fianna were to be reunited with their dear brother Dermot. Dermot told his children stories about the Fianna and they fought mock battles and learned many songs to sing when the feast finally came to their door. At last, the time to be happy had come.

Exactly a year after the invitation, Finn arrived with the Fianna in tow. You can imagine how eager they all were to get a look at each other. Grainne was sure Finn would be a stooped old man by now and Dermot was expecting to help his former lord up the stairs with a hand on the elbow. To their surprise, Finn didn't look much older than the last time they'd seen him, but they could see in his eyes that they had aged. Grainne was no longer the most beautiful maid in the kingdom about to be married to a middle-aged king. She was a married woman, still beautiful, but the weight of her years was starting to show on her.

And so the feast began, bards reciting poetry, never an empty goblet, roasted swan on the table, and the warmth of conversation kept the hall so warm they forgot that outside the snow was piling up. Peace wasn't so bad after all.

But was this peace? Dermot still tossed and turned in his sleep. Finn still sat awake long nights staring into the dark. One night when the moon was dark, it was time for the reckoning they all longed for. Enough.

Dermot and Grainne awoke to the sound of a horn and hounds on the hill. Grainne clutched at Dermot when he shifted to get out of bed. "Stay here, my darling. That's something sent out of fairy, I'm sure of it." But Dermot was dressed and out the bedchamber door as if he'd never been married or fathered children before she could say another word.

Spear in hand, he climbed up Mount Bulben, following the baying hounds until he found Finn himself, not the fairy court. "What's this, Finn? You don't have my permission to hunt on this land." If Finn MacCool bristled at this, he kept it secret, replying calmly, "Oh no, nothing like that, just wandering the hills with the boys. You used to love that, remember? Out in the night with the wind and stars, cracking jokes, telling stories."

"Yes, but why the hounds? What's going on?"

"Ah yes, you heard them. The hounds have caught the scent of a boar—absolutely gigantic—I just got a glimpse of him. You should see him. Probably the biggest I've ever seen. A legend in these parts. The men ran after him with the hounds but I know better. They'll never catch him. I'm just sitting here waiting to see who comes tumbling back down the mountain."

A legendary boar! Hunting with the Fianna! Dermot's blood stirred like an owl hunting a field mouse. His domestic trance was shattered. He had to join the hunt. "To hounds!" he cried.

Finn tried to dissuade him. "Stay out of the fray, Dermot.

You know you're not so young yourself anymore." Of course, this had the opposite effect. Finn was no fool. "I never retreat," Dermot retorted. "You of all men should know that, Finn. To hounds!" he yelled again and spun away from his chief in the direction of the baying, hurtling up the mountain where a great beast was about to turn and charge back down, the boar of Ben Bulben. If he had waited just a second longer he might have heard Finn whisper, "Ah, Dermot, I was afraid you'd say something like that."

The Fianna rushed down the rumbling mountain behind the boar who was knocking trees down in its blind rage. When the beast exploded into a clearing, Dermot was there surging toward the fight, putting himself right in its path as the hunters swept past him to safety. Dermot loosed his hound, but when the dog saw what was coming, it slunk away. It was just him and the boar then.

Aengus Og didn't come this time, or any other of the magical creatures he'd met in his vagabond years. The beast was so ferocious all he could do was hurl his spear at its snout and pray to any gods that would hear him.

The spear didn't even break the skin of the bristly snout. The boar spun as Dermot circled. Whack! He brought his sword down on its rump. Snapped in two. Without a sword or the help of a god, he realized he was just a man after all. For the first time in his life, he knew terror. He would die on this mountain.

Inevitable as lust, the tusk entered, but the beast didn't kill him outright. The boar flung Dermot onto his back and took off. Miles and miles they crashed through the brush with Dermot clinging to the boar's bristles. They knocked down saplings and tore up tender roots. Some say they traveled back over the entire path Dermot had traveled with Grainne, returning finally to the base of Ben Bulben, the fateful mountain. There, the boar dumped Dermot off, and there, without ceremony or hesitation, before he could inhale or exhale, tusks raked him from groin to throat. His guts spilled out onto the soil of Erin.

At last, Dermot exhaled.

But who came walking out of the trees to find him on the ground? Finn MacCool, chief of the Fianna, great warrior and bard of Erin. Finn walked over to his best friend and said coolly, "What's this? Ah, Dermot. Looks like that boar got you good. I told you to stay back. Looks like the jig for you might finally be up."

Now if you'll remember, Finn's thumb had healing powers from the time he'd burned it on the skin of the Salmon of Knowledge. Anyone that drank water from his cupped hands would be rejuvenated, no matter how dire the wound. Clearly, Finn had forgotten this when he spoke to Dermot. It was too late for Dermot to remind his friend and chief. He had already slipped beyond speech. His voice was a death rattle.

Ossian knew, though, Finn's son by the deer woman, and when he saw his father standing over the dying Dermot, chatting away about consequence and chickens coming home to roost, rambling about the sixteen years he'd lost chasing him and Grainne, and the shame of being a cuckold, he was horrified.

"When did I ever show you anything but love Dermot?" Ossian heard his father say. Much to the mens' surprise, Dermot managed to speak. "Finn, my chief, you know I only betrayed you because I was under geis. Save my life, I beg you. Bring me water from your healing hands."

"Where would I get water out here in the forest, Dermot?" Finn said in a calm, bemused way.

Ossian couldn't hold back any longer, "Dad! There is a spring not nine paces from you! You are bigger than this. Be the miracle you are. For all you have been to me my whole life bring this man you love the water of life!"

Finn pretended to be surprised at the nearby spring, when in fact he'd heard it with his salmon senses gurgling all this time. He'd known it was there when he sat waiting on the mountain for Dermot to answer the hound's cry. He strolled to the pool and scooped water in his hands, bending toward his dear friend. Looking into the dying Dermot's eyes he said, "Alas, I have some cruelty still in me. You did that, my friend," and opened his palms to let the water fall to the earth.

Ossian, desolate, cried out, "Dad! If you don't save him I'll never talk to you again!" To his relief, Finn turned and walked back to the pool. Taking his time there and back, he bent once again with cupped hands to Dermot's lips and... opened his palms again. He couldn't do it. By now the rest of the Fianna had gathered and were weeping at the sight of their brother Dermot gored from groin to throat, with his steaming guts spilling out. Ossian was beyond horror, he was heartbroken. He didn't yell, only said in a stunned voice, "Dad, this is the moment your whole life has been building to—right now, right here. You must save him. Change this story, bring Dermot the water of life."

Something in Ossian's voice shook Finn. He turned and headed back to the spring, this time running. For the third time, he bent to the spring and cupped the water, sprinting back to Dermot. With his healing hands just inches away from his friend's lips—Dermot expired.

Finn, grave and silent, watched the life leave his eyes. The weeping of the Fianna was a terrible sound that traveled all the way to the castle to Grainne in their bedchamber. The bed was still warm from Dermot's body, the sheets and pillows smelled of him. He was dead. Nobody wept like that for someone still living.

Finn made his way back to her, catching Dermot's staghound that had run off on the way, called by the passing of his master's spirit. Finn leashed the hound. Ossian and Oscar and the rest of the Fianna covered Dermot's maimed body with a cloak and keened as the sun rose giving them nowhere to hide their grief. It seemed like the whole mountain was mourning the death of Dermot O'Duibhne.

Grainne was waiting for Finn at the gates. When she saw him holding Finn's hound by the leash she knew it was true, what she'd heard in the hounds' baying. "Please leave me his hound at least," she asked Finn MacCool. "I don't think so," he said looking in her eyes without malice. He had moved beyond that to a colder place. "The hound stays with me." Finn turned, and with leashed hound in hand, began to leave that desperate scene. He stopped. Grainne's lips trembled. Finn turned his head and said over his shoulder, "Satisfied?"

Years passed. Grainne was not really cut out for selfless mother-hood. She filled her children's heads with stories of Dermot so that he became almost a god to them. One by one they left the nest to train as magicians and warriors so they could avenge their father. Grainne sat alone now by her fire with only her memories of how she used to sit there with Dermot for company.

One frigid winter night: a knock at the door. Who's this? A cloaked stranger was admitted. The servants escorted him to the fire where he removed it and there, standing before the woman who had rejected him so long ago, was Finn MacCool.

Grainne wanted nothing to do with him. "How dare you!" she hissed, but he refused to leave. He waited. He waited through the servants heaping buckets of dung on him. He waited through a fever that wracked him for days; he almost didn't survive that. He waited until he was gaunt, the way a child would wait for his parents to come back from their execution. Only no one was coming back. They both knew it. Finally, Grainne relented and asked for him to be brought to her by the fire. She looked at him. Haggard, grizzled, red-eyed from a lifetime of tears finally loosed. She knew she didn't look much better. Grief had had its way with her, too. The wrinkles in her cheeks may have been the tracks of tears. Her hair now was more white than yellow, though it was hard to tell because it still shone, but like the moon now, cool and contemplative. She could barely remember how she'd burned like the sun in her youth. All that trouble led to this: stuck again with Finn Mac-Cool by a fire that never completely warmed her bones. "What is it then? Why this mooning at my door?" she snapped, afraid she would cry herself.

It took a few moments for Finn to gather himself, but when he spoke his voice was steady. "There are so few of us left who remember him, Grainne." At that, his voice cracked and a fist clenched Grainne's heart. She mustn't cry. She must hold tight to her dream of vengeance.

Finn spoke again into the space hollowed out by their shared grief, "Tell me a story about him—anything. Some adventure from your years together in the woods or the way you two loved to sit by this very fire. I only want to hear his name spoken in the air once again by someone who loved him. Let the rest fall away. Let's be done. Remember him with me, our Dermot of the Love Spot. Bring him back with your words, Grainne. Just for a moment let us live once again in the enchanted grace of his presence."

Grainne said nothing for a long time. Finn didn't pressure her. The embers stirred and a white flame flickered back into life. Grainne looked closer as the flame shifted from orange to white to blue, remembering the heat of Dermot, the way she'd felt as a twelve-year-old girl that first time she saw him, and all the times after. For her, his beauty had never faded. The enchantment never broke.

Rain began to fall. "I remember when..." she began. Finn looked at her far-seeing eyes with a soft smile. At last, man and wife, Finn and Grainne lived together for the rest of their lives.

When I finish the story I can feel my ancestors crowding behind me hoping to get a glimpse in what little water remains.

Our bones carry us through Earth life, provide structure

and form for spirit to enter with grace. Babies are born with a soft spot in their skulls, the fontanelle, so the soul can enter through this soft place; the pelvis separates when a woman gives birth. Even bones are fluid.

Van Morrison on the car radio on the way back uphill:

> If I ventured in the slipstream.
> Between the viaducts of your dream.
> Where immobile steel rims crack
> and the ditch in the back roads stop
> Could you find me?
> Would you kiss-a my eyes?
> To lay me down
> in silence easy
> to be born again
> to be born again

The spotlight shines on the dead girl's memorial. I catch a flash of bright flowers as I pass in the dark.

CHAPTER 20
MACROCOSMIC VISIONS FROM A BLACK HOLE

@

TODAY IN MINNEAPOLIS, police officer Derek Chauvin was convicted in the murder of George Floyd. Chauvin, a white man, kneeled on the neck of Floyd, a black man, for nine minutes and 29 seconds. A bystander in front of Cup Foods began recording.

"I can't breathe," Floyd managed to say, then, "Please... Mama."

Today in the ocean off Kukio, a 57-year-old woman was bitten by a tiger shark while swimming. She lived.

And today the pond is more mud than water. The diameter has shrunk to maybe ten feet, and in the center, what should be the deepest part, the water is only two or three inches deep.

Fish cluster in the mouth-scooped depressions like refugees, yet miraculously, the King and Queen are still in motion, keeping the water alive as they loop and weave. The sky is so dull their skin is the same color as the water.

Only one day left in this ceremony. I find myself wanting something spectacular to conclude, some affirmation that this little world has heard me. The female fish school in place, barely moving their fins to keep water flowing over their gills.

The water is low enough to expose my original vigil spot, the stone where I first saw Crabby and Big Papa. Big Papa is here, cleaning his love nest one mouthful of sand at a time. He is still solo. In the next bunker over, his rival shakes his tail above a shuddering female.

Why him and not Big Papa? He is so handsome with his red fins and jutting lips. I'm sure he knows how to shimmy and shake. Maybe there is some biological reason I can't see, but I do know there is no explaining desire, despite what biologists say about pheromones.

I began this story as a Fool and here we are on Judgment Day and there's nobody but me to reckon with. It's true. I was a fool. I followed my heart and believed nothing could harm me as long as I was confident. I was so confident I was able to fool myself I wasn't in danger, though I knew from the minute I met his eyes I was. I was brash in my youth and beauty.

I took off my clothes at the waterfall and dove in the milk-green water after he told me the story about the shark boy, didn't blush when he told me how he and his brothers used to hide in the falls above and watch the hippie girls swim naked. I didn't look over my shoulder when he dove in after me. He stayed under so long. I should have known. I did know. I wanted him anyway.

Persephone so innocently picking flowers one afternoon, the next moment in the arms of Hades. She didn't choose, but I did. Make no mistake, I chose the 40oz. Steinlagers around the beach fire, the pakalolo, the cocaine in cane fields, the rough sex against rusted-out cars abandoned in the ironwood pines that scraped my belly. I wanted to appear tough, but I was fragile as a bird with one leg who forgot it had wings. I could have flown, but how would I land again?

Sometimes there is still a cane knife at my throat. Sometimes I'm still being dragged facedown by my feet back to the cabin where I will play dead on a cot in the corner while he paces across the old carpet making the floorboards squeak. Sometimes I still rise from the cot because it's too quiet and open the screen door onto the porch and see him standing on a chair with a noose around his neck roped to a rafter, and I am on my knees with my arms around his thighs begging him not do it, lifting, lifting.

And then I am loosening the noose and his bones lose their form, turn to jelly. They won't hold him up so I have to. I must be swift and delicate, slide the rope over his nose and skull before the rage returns.

And though I want to untie the rope from the beam right away so that option is gone, I leave it looped and hanging, because he is on his knees in front of me, sobbing into my belly. All I feel is how much he hates himself, not how close I came to death, so that even after this when I'm bleeding in the stream, our future gone, and sob, "It hurts!" and he says, "Did you think it wouldn't?" I believe I deserve it.

He may have turned his rage toward me, fucking stupid haole, but he hated himself more. I saw it on my last day in the valley—the total defeat. He had dragged me back by the feet when I tried to run that night. In daylight, he let me go. He even helped me, borrowing his mother's car to drive me to the airport.

On the way to Kona, we stopped at his grandparents' house to say goodbye, and his grandfather, who I wasn't sure even liked me, came to the door and gave me a ti leaf lei to bless my journey and a hundred dollars. He had tears in his eyes.

This quiet, humble man was a local legend. For years he'd trekked from Waipi'o to Waimanu, hauling his harvest by mules. He'd seen the tsunami of '47 from the z-trail, watched the monstrous wave sweep through the valley, swallowing Paka'alana, the other Place of Refuge where I so foolishly slept when I first came to the valley. He carried stories within stories going back hundreds of years that bound him to the ʻaina. Why was he sad I was leaving? I had no experience of such generosity.

We didn't talk in the car. The braided lei around my neck smelled fresh with green life. *Just keep going,* I prayed as we came closer to Ronny Guy's house, but I knew he would pull in the driveway.

"Can I have the money?" he asked. It was too late. I wanted to live. I handed it over.

He came out with the little white packet, the baking soda and tin foil. We sat in the driveway and he completed the ritual, mixing the coke with soda and water, spreading the paste on tinfoil, and cooking it from below until it sizzled. I can still smell the white smoke he inhaled through a toilet paper tube, sugar-sweet, synthetic, like burning plastic at the edge of a jungle. The smell of shame. Kekoa howled on his chain in the concrete yard.

The valley was only a couple of hours from the Kona airport. How far that seemed. His grandfather's tears followed us as we drove past the eucalyptus forests in Waimea, and then we were in the sun driving with the windows down right up to the airport tarmac. I wore the ti leaf lei the entire flight.

THE MEMORY GHOSTS

Tutu, bird woman,
you keep the valley alive
from a corner of the sofa,
a scratchy nest
I never see you leave.

Your fingers plait ti leaves.
Braided flowers in purple and green
bloom in your gnarled hands.

An ever-present flock of children
cackles and chirps like mynahs.

Your daughter Haulani
yells from the lanai,
stomping in rubber boots
around the yard,
trying to keep it all together.

Tutu, you hold the river
bencath your tongue,
your human voice
run underground by the TV
and the screaming kids
and Haulani ordering
everyone around except Jeremiah,
the kids' dad
who smokes cocaine
in the carport
with the neighborhood guys.

His friends stop by
talk story
take a hit. Inside

the women pretend
they don't know what's happening
outside, until Haulani
yells out the window—
"Stop doing dat white stuff!"
then goes back to stomping
because nothing will change.

I sit with you on the plaid sofa,

without a child
to follow me from room to room.

You are full-blooded Hawaiian
with the blunt nose of a shark
and the lips of an eel
deep in the reef.

You have lost the fat
of your prime, the belly
of a people raised on pork and poi,
the waterfall of your hair
cropped like Hi'ilawe,
a twin waterfall,
one stream dammed
by the sugar company.

Tutu, when you turn to me and say,
"We go Waipi'o. We go my house.
"You stay wit' me,"
 I know you can see
I've brought your ancestors to visit
on the soles of my bare feet.

Your house is long gone.
Gulches in your face
bear witness,
but
your face glows,
a kukui nut
cracked open.

When lit, the oil within
reveals Paka'alana,

the lost Place of Refuge,
swept away by a tsunami.

"Stop doing dat white stuff!"
Haulani yells out the window.
Mynahs cackle in the plumeria trees.
"Yes, let's go," I say.

Invisible hands place leis
gathered in the high gulches
ovcr our heads. Ghosts

lean in, inhale
the scent of maile.
Ferns dance on the breeze,
the breath of memory
carried through time
on living heartbeats.

Something big moves on the hillock across from me. Auku'u, the black-crowned night heron from the first day. Its blood-red eyes reveal nothing more than the patience required to sit and wait.

'Ulili dashes across my sight-line. How do birds disappear so quickly? It's like the sky swallows them up. Big Papa is still hard at work, carrying grains of sand up the slopes of his under-water crater. Two minnow-size fish, little scamps, dart into his territory every time he leaves, and dart back out as soon as he re-enters. I watch two other males face off over a female. She chooses Lover #1—for today at least.

A crab inches out from behind a rock, and for the first time, I notice tiny spiders leaping on the black rock by my feet. "Wel-come to the story," I say. Every now and then, the King and Queen reveal themselves, remaining dignified under the pressure of the rapidly dwindling water, they weave and pirouette like courtiers aware they will soon be fed to the guillotine.

Today is so gray it's like sitting inside a shadow. There won't be a visible sunset. The heron is waiting for me to leave. Time to hunt. Nothing sentimental about it. He's hungry.

Dusk is also the time of day the sleeping sharks awake and slip out of their caves to stalk the reef.

What if the water disappears overnight and there is none in the pond for the last day of the ceremony? What if the water knocks down the Great Wall and no one remembers the great King Keawe and how anyone who made it here by swimming across the bay could find sanctuary?

We have forgotten so much. Isn't it time to begin remembering?

Today, all the stories I told are alive in this air and this water will remember them, and when the tide pulls the ponds back through black lava they will be one again with the mother of all stories, the sea. She will carry them on currents, sweep them through channels and straits. They will wash up on beaches in whale corpses, stinking of mystery. Crabs will eat them.

These stories are food. My ancestors feast. *Well done,* I hear them say. *You survived. Let the end be a new beginning.*

In the night, a dream finds me. This is what happens:

I hit two women on my bike. Ride smack into them. The first is going downhill. The other is at the bottom waiting for an elevator to go up. Both women have shadowy entourages I can't quite see. Ancestors? The two old women silence them. I apologize and offer reparations, but they shush me.

"We just want you to know," they say as one. "You've reached the piko."

In the dream I don't know what that is, but I'm delighted we all see a rainbow. I leave them and jump back on my bike. I ride through a garage and there is my old friend Turtle, an actual human, not the honu I've been hoping to catch a glimpse of this entire ceremony.

"Hi, Turtle!" I shout with glee. "Hi Jennifer!" he answers, just the way he does whenever I cruise by his garage workshop on Old Town Road on Block Island. Sometimes the spirits show up however they must.

I remember piko is the word for belly button, but Hawaiian words always have multiple meanings. I look it up and discover the piko is the source of all existence, the world's navel, plus a bunch of other practical things like a hat with no crown so you can shade your eyes with your hair piled on top of your head. In Waipi'o, crazy high on pakalolo, we would laugh sometimes until we couldn't breathe, and my boyfriend would kiss me in that tender place that had once joined me to my mother.

Anuenue, Rainbow Maiden, mahalo for this dream. Thank you. I remember. I remember it all, the violence and the beauty. I choose to see them both. I walk out of the valley's shadow, knowing that on those nights when he cooked me prawns he pulled out from under river rocks, and fiddlebacks we picked in the ferns above our heads after we'd bathed in the sunken tub and washed our hair with awapui, walking back to sit on the porch with the cats next to the purple jacaranda to look up at Hi'ilawe with mud from the taro patch etched on our palms, we became part of the valley's dreaming. There was a price to pay— for all the breathtaking beauty, a violence to equal its force. I came close to death because I wanted to live that much, to fully inhabit my body and experience the wave and the waterfall with every molecule. Raised in a culture that had no concept this was even possible, it took the shock of violence to wake my cells and senses up. It wasn't personal.

The Mu doctrines say that on this planet, every invocation must be balanced by a sacrifice. If we don't choose the sacrifice,

Ka Mea Nāna i Hana, Creator, will choose it for us, and it may be far from pleasant. It will be fair, though, equal in force to our desire. But what if you have no clue what you want, or even that you want something in the first place? That was the place from which I descended into the valley.

If someone had asked me, I probably would have said I wanted to be a writer. I was seeking experiences to write about, which is one of the reasons I so often sat like a fly on the wall in what many would say were insane situations, but that's not what I really wanted. What I really wanted was to unveil my soul, to express the depths of myself I couldn't yet reach, for which I didn't have words. What I wanted was to be a poet.

In almost sacrificing the body Creator had given me, I also invoked my purpose, calling my soul through beauty and violence back into my body in what may be the first lifetime in generations. Like all of us, my ancestral lineage, and my soul's, has been scarred by catastrophe. The natural processes of Earth—floods and earthquakes, volcanoes and tsunamis, led to warriors hacking down whole villages from horseback, rape, enslavement, nobody feeling safe on Earth and not understanding why.

Why did we have to evolve through cataclysm? I can speculate about that, but I don't want to stop the flood of tears.

Ola i ka wai a ka 'ōpua. There is life in the water from the clouds. I was willing to die to stop this cycle. It was not intentional.

I anointed my scarred lineage with libations of blood and tears, the fluids of *this* body my ancestors gave me, passing down their DNA through sexual fluids and semen. Milk and honey dripped from the seat of my soul down the stem of my spine, and now I am an open flower, the serpent gazes out through my eyes.

I weave a spell with my hands on this keyboard that travels back and forth along time, replenishing the starved roots with holy nutrients. I banish my amnesia.

As I remember where I came from, the piko widens, includes you—He waiwai nui ka lōkahi—Unity is a precious possession. I know when the time comes for us to pass through the hole at the bottom into the next world, I won't be alone.

In the next world, instead of being crushed in the birth canal, we won't lose *all* the truth of ourselves through amnesia. Maybe some of it, we are not the ones in charge of evolution's course, but not all. Enough to choose wonder, not shame as our guide, as we create the next world. We won't need violence to wake us up. We'll slip out of the womb remembering who we are and not be afraid of the dark anymore.

CHAPTER 21
THE MOVEMENT OF A PRAYER

THE WATER has returned. On the ceremony's last day, lost in reverie, I didn't even notice until it soaked my pants' leg. A half dozen minnows look up at me. I slide my foot toward the minnows and as soon as it's submerged, they begin nibbling my toes, a dead skin feast.

To my right, a tiny waterfall pours over the ledge toward me. The change from desert to oasis is fast. It can happen like that. Sometimes it's easy.

Ka'ape'ape is the fern of Grace and helps move our prayers. Watching the ponds fill, I know someone has heard me these past 21 days. And I have heard myself as part of everything.

The ponds deepen. From my seat on the bridge between them, I watch fish cluster in the center of the body of water to the left, tails down and lips above the surface, they drink the air. Or maybe they are singing. I dip my fingers in and lick them. Salty. I finally understand where the water is coming from. The ocean, two hundred yards away, is flowing through the lava field, through rock itself, to fill these depressions. The water comes and goes with the tide. I have learned something essential about this place without looking it up in a book.

This has been happening for centuries before there were people to measure time, but today I'm here to see it. How the rocks and water shape themselves to each other. A big fish jumps in the larger pond. Two red-headed cardinals land in the shrubs and peep.

Tonight I will dream of the whales singing their way home, and pray they can hear each other through the monstrous roar of ships and underwater bombs. So much has been lost, yet the King and Queen of the Pond have woven their shining loops all this time when it seemed they would soon be gills up in mud. The water has returned. The stories will go on.

Three male fish gather in the same sand crater right in front of me. Big Papa's made some friends. A dragonfly—first I've seen this whole time—helicopters over the pond and disappears. I remember the white snails I saw on the first day of the ceremony. I haven't seen them this whole time. Do they only appear on rare moons or did I witness their extinction? I hope my presence here has been for them a drink of sweet water.

I have two stories today, one for each pond. I face left and let the words pour out of me.

UKEMOCHI

At the beginning of time, Amaterasu gave life to the world. She was a sun goddess and ruled over the sky with her brother, the moon god Tsukuyomi.

From her perch in the sky, Amaterasu heard of another goddess who lived down below on Earth named Ukemochi, and decided she wanted to send her a greeting from the sky. She asked her brother, Ashihara-no-Nakatsukuni, to make the journey down to the Central Land of Reed-Plains, for that is what they called the blue planet spinning beneath them, and bring Ukemochi her celestial greetings. Tsukuyomi was happy to oblige and descended to Earth.

Ukemochi, a humble goddess, maybe a little shy, was thrilled to have such a noble visitor. In most stories, gods and goddesses have servants to prepare their elaborate banquets. I'm sure you've heard of many, like the fateful feast held by Dermot and Grainne for Finn MacCool and the Fianna. The servants prepared for months. A feast is hard, hot work, not something fit for a goddess.

When Ukemochi invited Tsukuyomi to a feast, he said yes, but looking around her hall was a bit dubious. Where were the servants? Surely, she wasn't going to cook for herself? He was even more confused when he showed up at the banquet table and found it empty.

Wanting to be polite, he smiled and said nothing. Ukemochi gave him a slight bow. The moon god was at her table! The honor was almost too much. She returned his smile, excited to present him with a feast to honor his greatness.

You can imagine Tsukuyomi's shock when Ukemochi faced a rice field outside the hall and turned toward him vomiting boiled rice!

It got worse. Next, she faced the sea and disgorged fish of all kinds from her gullet. Tsukuyomi was trying to maintain a polite façade, but he was starting to gag. He was expected to eat this? When next she turned to a forest and expelled all kinds of game—deer and rabbits, his eyes almost popped out of his head. The game was cooked and ready to eat. It was too much. He looked at Amaterasu and could see she was very pleased with herself. He drew his sword and killed her.

When he returned to the sky and told Amaterasu what he'd done he didn't expect her to be angry, so angry in fact she told him she would never again meet him face to face. That is why, all the way to this day, the Sun and Moon are never seen together.

Amaterasu sent another messenger down to the terrestrial world to check on Ukemochi's people. It was her fault she had died, she would take care of her sister goddesses' people if she had to.

When the messenger came back, she carried a surprising story.

The people on Earth didn't need her help, for Ukemochi's body, all on its own, had sprouted all kinds of food for them to eat. From her head came the ox and horse; from her forehead, millet; from her eyebrows, silkworms; from her eyes, cereal grass; from her belly, rice; and from her genitals, wheat, and beans. The grains were sown so people could have plenty to feed themselves.

They still needed Amaterasu, of course, all crops need sun to flourish, but from then on the people began to remember the power of their own choices. Amaterasu admired their resilience and decided to give them a gift herself.

From the cocoons of the silkworms Ukemochi had disgorged from her eyebrows, Amaterasu spun silk thread. The crafty humans spun this thread into diaphanous cloth that rippled in the sun's light. It looked fragile but was very strong. People on Earth still weave the silkworm's cocoons into this beautiful fabric. When they dye it, it becomes a vessel for all the colors of the sun. People on Earth still eat the food Ukemochi created from her own dead body. Some people may have forgotten this, but whenever someone remembers, a song from a bamboo flute drifts up toward the moon. Some say the song is sad, a mournful dirge, but others know it is the sound of contentment, not a lament, but the hymn of a life filled with purpose.

I sit quietly under my black umbrella. It's not raining hard enough to really need it, but I need a boundary. Four tourists have stopped on the path to watch my back. *Please, let us keep this place sacred,* I silently implore them. I make myself small and hope they move along. They talk loudly, sensing my resistance. The polite thing would be to turn around and answer their questions. Facts and figures and what-are-you-doings. "Look! Fish!" they shout. I cringe.

But I don't own this place. No one does, despite the fact that the US government has claimed it as a National Park. *There are so many of us,* I want to say to the humans, *so few fish and the white snails have not been seen in three weeks.* I soften and try to make my silence friendly. They move on.

The calm deepens as if never disturbed. One more story. One from *this* land, Hawai'i, whose water and rock, whose liquid fire, has held me as I learned how to praise.

THE BIRTH OF HALOA

Before humans came to the Hawaiian Islands the land was ruled by fire, water, and wind. Humuhumunukunukuapua`a in the reefs could speak to i'iwi birds high up the mountains singing in the ohia lehua. Waterfalls cycled all the wisdom of Earth downslope into roots who sent it back up to the sky through trees whose roots hummed to the moon's rhythms.

Wakea, Father Sky, and Papa, Mother Earth, ruled over all. They had a beautiful daughter named Ho'ohokulani, whose name meant The Making of Stars in the Heavens. Just saying it you could feel her beauty. Wakea fell in love with her, and in time he and his daughter, The Making of Stars in Heaven, conceived a child. The family waited patiently for the birth.

The baby was stillborn. A boy. They named him Haloa— long, eternal breath. "He looks like a root," the kūpuna said when they saw him, so they wrapped his body in kapa, placed him in a woven lauhala basket, and buried his bones in the 'aina.

Ho'ohokulani, daughter of Papa and Wakea, grieved. She

wept over her son's grave, and her tears watered the soil covering the small root of who he would have become.

One day as she cried, a sprout pushed its way up through the hard mound. The sprout needed water, so she kept on weeping. Slowly, it reached for the light and became a strong green shoot. Watching the stem grow heart-shaped leaves cleaved her own heart. She kept on weeping. This plant was new to Honua, to Earth. It was strong and tender. She named the leaves: lau kapalili, tremble leaf; and lau kapalala, broad leaf. The center of each leaf was a cup filled with teardrops.

She sensed when the plant swelled underground and began to divide itself, and when the roots formed tubers, the people fed themselves on them. Kalo was born. The tubers grew in clumps, little underground families. Ho'ohokulani carefully broke the stems off each clump and replanted it in the mud. Another plant grew and the people followed her example, returning part of the plant each time they harvested.

Ho'ohokulani conceived again and this time gave birth to a living son she also named Haloa. She started calling her first son Haloa Naka so people wouldn't be confused. Haloa Naka became the respected elder brother to Haloa. Haloa became the first Hawaiian. All children after that were given names like we have today, but they were known first as keiki o ka 'aina, children of the land.

Some still remember that people and nature were born from the same parents at the beginning of time, but many have forgotten. It is time now to remember how we came to be here on this confusing place called Earth where typhoons destroy our crops, tsunamis our villages and nuclear power plants, where hurricanes flatten apartment buildings and floods lift whole houses off their foundations and carry them downriver. It is time for us to remember what we all knew at the beginning, before chiefs and ali'i, kings and queens and dukes, robber barons and senators, tech bros and Instagram influencers. In the beginning, we were all the common people, the maka'ainana, the eyes of the land. Despite our differences, we still are.

E mālama pono i ka' aina. Take good care of the Earth. Life depends on us as much as we depend on it, and even today, it's said if there's no poi for the table, Haloa will die. When Haloa dies, we all do.

Across the left pond, the Tree of Knowledge, stripped of its frond crown, juts like a skyscraper into the sky. I let the black umbrella fall.

> I am the trilling birds in the naupaka.
> I am the chattering mynah high in the palm.
> I am a fish listening to a story,
> a crab scuttling sideways through mud.
> I am the rock that began as liquid fire,
> sea purslane that lives in air
> and underwater.

> I am the ripples on the water
> and the sound of splashing.
> I am the thunder of the waterfall.

> I am the red-finned fish
> kissing the air,
> the fork-tailed mullet
> weaving my spells in shallow water.

> I am a King.
> I am a Queen.
> I am the trees reflected in the pond
> and their reflections.

I am the cracked mud,
the cleansing rain.
I am light on water.

I am the give and take of clouds,
the red-eyed auku'u,
the bobbing 'ulilli,
the pueo on my roof.

I am the dreaming honu
waiting for the moon's dark side
to reveal itself,
to cleanse my shell
at the secret source of water.

I am every story told
and ones that haven't
been dreamed yet.

I am fire underwater,
the rising island.
Loihi is my name.
In 200,000 years
when I break the ocean's surface,
harden into land,
who will be the first to root?

I am blessed
and I am a blessing,
the red hibiscus opened fully to the sun,
the night blooming jasmine
perfuming the dark
with fulfilled promise.

I am the covenant of the rainbow,

the white dove.

I am the daughter of loss,
the son of shame,
the mother of grief
who ends in completion,
when the father I am
engenders a new lineage.

I am my ancestors.
I move their unfulfilled prayers
with grace. I am that I am.
I offer my bones to the unknown.

Somewhere in the future
a woman reaches into two pools
and fills her cup with starlight,
pours it back and forth
without spilling a drop.
When she offers me a drink,
in the water's shining
I regard my own goodness.
I am worthy.

He ku'upau,
Jesus said as he died on the cross.
It is accomplished.

I was here.
I beheld the world
as best as I could
and praised it.

aloha mā aloha mā aloha mā

It's time for the final offering.

Jada, when we met that first morning at Two-Step, the tourist name, a dimensional overlay for the sacred Honaunau Bay that has held this ceremony these past 21 days, we were two currents moving in different directions in the same stream in the middle of the tourist chaos. I was entering the water, you were getting out. I had no idea what that was going to really mean in just a few short weeks. Maybe you did, but up until your last days you still expressed, even after the doctors told you to prepare yourself for dying, you still weren't sure if you were coming or going. Perhaps, for you, they were the same.

I don't know either, but I'm holding some of your ashes right now in a mason jar. I twist the lid and open it, look down, and have a hard time believing your warm skin has been reduced to this. How can this be you? Your tenderness and wonder and beauty? You don't answer me, so I answer my heart's cry to make something beautiful with this handful of dust you've become. I touch you, dip my finger in and swirl. Your ashes are gritty. You earned them.

Sifting, my finger snags on bone. The solid truth of it. I open my palms and you become a white moth fluttering toward the moon, a comet with a flashing tail, and when you settle into a cloud on the water you're not a reflection. The cloud whirls, unresisting. The water speaks in whirlpools.

I turn to the other pond and unfurl my hands like ferns in a forest clearing. *I love you, Jada.* Ashes stick to my skin. I dip my hands in the water and you are gone. *You have no idea how much I love you,* she'd told me. Now I understand.

When I leave Big Papa is removing bone flecks from his territory, one mouthful at a time, ever hopeful.

I pass back through the Great Wall for the final time and walk through the park toward my car as if I'm in a dream. My feet know the way in the dark over the white gravel.

In the parking lot, I'm met by chorusing birds and noisy

mynahs bedding down for the night in a gigantic jacaranda. A whirligig of motion draws my gaze skyward. There is something off about this bird's flight.

The black shape drops closer. This is not a bird, or a drone, or a gigantic nocturnal insect. It's a bat, pe'ape'a—rare in Hawai'i. This is the first one I've ever seen. Instinctively I shudder, but manage to hold still and not flail my arms above my head to beat it away.

There is only one species of bat in Hawai'i and it's endemic. The ancestors of this bat found their way to this most remote landmass on Earth, on their own. It's a solitary sort, not like those bats that pour by the thousands out of dusky caves and culverts in Texas.

People are saying bats may be the source of the coronavirus, transmitted to pangolins they bit in the jungle that ended up in China's wet markets, where live animals are killed on site for human consumption.

> Pe'ape'a,
> black madonna
> hanging upside down on cave walls
> nursing your young
> until they can wing through the dark
> on sound like dolphin sonar.
>
> What do you hear ahead of us?
> Will we all die
> with no one left to mourn us?
>
> Or could we accept the shadow,
> praise Ereshkigal
> as much as Inanna,
> become the living water,
> walk between worlds to learn

the open secret that will save us—
the future is now.

On the other side of the Great Wall, palm branches reach across the gap between their trunks and touch above the black stones. The Tree of Life enfolds the Tree of Knowledge. In the ponds, two fork-tailed mullet loop in figure-eights through the shimmering water.

We will go down further. Not all of us will make it back.

But some will. The bat drops even closer, whirls like a Sufi dervish above the crown of my head, another piko, the soft part of a baby's skull where the soul enters.

Pe'ape'a rises on webbed wings and flies west, tracking the sun. Here in the Pu'uhonua o Hōnaunau, I make this final ho'okukāla: Moku o Keawe, you have claimed me. I am the Place of Refuge.

Āmama ua noa

Now the prayer has flown

THE TOTALITY
AN EPILOGUE

☺

BREATHING AGAIN AFTER A LONG TIME UNDERWATER

Reaching my hands into the late afternoon light
glowing on the river's final curve, I didn't believe
I was beautiful,
                      like the valley's wild horses
hiding in high ferns I parted with my hands like
lace curtains, air
closing behind me without a ripple.

I came to a clearing.   Light streamed down.

From the far side a mare rose from crushed ferns.
She watched me with the liquid eyes of one
who can see in the dark without stumbling.

I wanted to come closer, but her foal,
still in its slick caul, stood on shaky legs,
fell back onto ferns slippery with birth blood.

For a few moments I forgot I was a human
who could kill what I loved.

At dusk I bathed at the river's edge
where the horses came out of the ironwoods
to face the river's mouth. Sharks waited there
for pig carcasses to wash down,
jaws hacked out by hunters to mount.

People disappeared all the time in that valley.

I was just a girl at the edge of a clearing.

I don't need to tell the story of how I was
broken anymore.
                    Now I can speak
of how a wild horse watched me from the ironwoods
and of how warm the river was when I knelt
to lift late afternoon light out of the water.

                How I

poured it over my head. How it flowed
down my hair and shoulders, gilding my skin,
                    returned to river unbroken.

AFTERWORD

HO'OKUKĀLA: A PROCLAMATION

I have bent time with my attention, channeled worlds with words, and moved beyond the limits of my skin without losing myself. I have crossed oceans and come back to the black-crowned night heron who holds me in his blood-red eye, stepping out of the long grass into the open. The story is not over. It never is. It's just changing form.

Inanna and Dumuzi live on. He gets his six months up here on Earth and doesn't bitch and moan about having to go back down to the Underworld. I imagine him giving Geshtinanna a high five as they swap places. When he's on this side he takes his place happily and doesn't try to get revenge on his wife. He may miss his sister and wish she was there to enjoy the wine, but he still enjoys the banquets; he performs the sacred rites. The text even tells us he does a lot of worshiping of Inanna's vulva! And there's no whining over fate from Geshtinanna either. What we do hear from them is praise, a song echoing through the banquet halls and temples of Sumer:

The place is festive. The King is joyous.
In the pure clean place they celebrate Inanna in song.
She is the ornament of the assembly, the joy of Sumer!
The people spend the day in plenty.
The king stands before the assembly in great joy.
He hails Inanna with the praises of the gods and
     the assembly:
"Holy Priestess! Created with the heavens and earth,
Inanna, First Daughter of the Moon, Lady of the Evening!
I sing your praises!"
My Lady looks in sweet wonder from heaven.
The people of Sumer parade before the holy Inanna.
The Lady Who Ascends into the Heavens, Innana,
     is radiant.
Mighty, majestic, radiant, and ever youthful—
To you, Inanna, I sing!

Even when we speak we are not really the ones telling the story. When we start out, we are like the heroes painted on clay-fired vessels. If we stand the heat long enough, we become the vessels themselves. There's no formula for this, but it helps to stop struggling. Don't try so hard to change the plot. You'll be amazed at what you'll discover, and most likely you'll realize that surrender will grant you more true agency than grabbing life by the balls. Willpower was meant to help us give our gifts to the world, not as a means to get what we want.

Remember the first story I told in this book, Nanaue the Shark Man? His father was Kamohoaliʻi, the shark god. Everyone was rightly terrified of him. He was also the keeper of the water of life. Fear can restore.

So many of us have lost our connection to the ancestral ceremonies that married us to the land, but we are still humans with ears to listen to the wind, feet to touch clay, and hands to shape vessels to hold water. The experiment called a human being is still ongoing. We just need to feel safe enough again to have faith in ourselves, faith that not only can we make it, but that we belong here as much as the herons and mullet, the 'ulilli and pueo, the millions of insects going extinct we take for granted.

We are needed. Earth, crying out to us from the Great Below, is summoning us down to the Underworld to sit in our collective shadow. We are her children much as the species we mourn—those already extinct and those about to be lost forever-the java tigers and black rhinos and giant ibises. Think of what Earth will lose if we, too, go extinct.

May my words soothe the breach between left and right, the brain and the body politic, and reunite logic with imagination and wonder. May the King and Queen loop forever in this water made sacred by my attention, and may the water know I have come to love it with the simplicity of contentment, sitting by its side for 21 days in the 21st year of the 21st century.

For a while, we'll have to give more than we take. By a while, I mean lifetimes, beyond mine and yours. It's the necessary correction if we are to go on, and by "we" I mean all of us— the tree-people, creepy crawlers, ocean dwellers, winged ones, stone-people, deer on the mountain, elephants on the savannah, lions in the sun, jaguars in the river, weasels on the edge of the ice, salmon-fishing grizzlies, clouds, butterflies, milkweed, worms, violets, plumeria. We need *all* the flowers, *all* the poems, *all* the songs, *all* the beautiful things. We need you.

And when despair hits, remember, it's never too late to give something. We've forgotten our being is created through images within images, layers of stories like rock going down to Earth's molten core. We are what's missing from the Earth's story. It's time to restore reciprocity.

Rilke said, "'Everywhere I am folded, I am a lie."

Let us become transparent as water so that when we gaze

into it we see beyond our own reflections to the unknown depths. Pa wale pu'uwai. *Open your heart wider.*

Let's be consistent. Let's show up. If not for ourselves, then for the gasping birds that wash up on beaches every time there's an oil spill and the dolphins rounded up for slaughter in Taiji. Show up for the bleached coral reefs and strip-mined mountaintops, and the polar bears who have to swim hundreds of miles to hunt because the ice has melted. Show up for children. That's what a worthy ancestor does.

Except for the Great Wall of China which is disintegrating back into Gobi dust, no walls can be seen when looking down from space on Earth. Mountains, rivers and oceans are the only visible borders.

Once upon a time, we had to walk or swim to cross these borders. Now we can fly right over them.

Before we could fly, we were more in touch with our bodies—we knew they could die from cold and lack of oxygen on the mountain, could drown in a flash flood, be swept out to sea by a riptide and never seen again. Because we knew how fragile we were, how permeable, we were more available to the natural world and to ourselves. We didn't need to find ourselves, we were where we were. We were mountain. We were river. We were ocean. We were the Place of Refuge.

THE STORIES

⊚

Nanaue the Shark Man, Hawaiian

The Name, Haitian

Birth of the Titans, Greek

The Rape of Medusa, Greek

Sedna, Inuit

The Salmon of Knowledge, Irish

The Moon Man, Chukchi

The Descent of Inanna, Sumerian

Psyche and Eros, Greek

Dumuzi's Dream, Sumerian

Hi'ilawe, Hawaiian

The Oldest Boy, Inuit

Pele and Kamapua'a, Hawaiian

The Wind from Ha'ena, Hawaiian

The Pursuit of Dermot and Grainne, Irish

Ukemochi, Japanese

The Birth of Haloa, Hawaiian

NOTES

INTRODUCTION

1. *Wolferland,* Martin Shaw, Cista Mystica Press, www.cistamystica.com

2. Anchialine ponds are unique aquatic ecosystems that form where water pools in cracks and crevices of lava near shore. The water is brackish, a mix of rain from the mountain and seawater moving through subterranean tunnels, they fluctuate with the tide. Highly endangered, they host life forms found nowhere else and are most commonly found on Hawai'i Island and Mexico's Yucatán Peninsula.

3. Heka, Mū Hawaiian magic, taught to me by Ke'oni Hanalei, of Mū Hawaiian lineage, founder of PōHALA Hawaiian Botanicals. www.pohala.net.

4. An abundance of incredible revelations from the Mū culture can be found at the PōHALA Hawaiian Botanicals website, www.pohala.net.

5. The Hawaiians recognize three energy centers in the human avatar: 'unihipili, uhane, and aumakua. These centers contain the feminine, masculine, and androgynous potential for each human and correspond to the sacral, heart and crown of head.

CHAPTER 1: WHAT'S THE NATURE OF MY GAME

1. "Sympathy for the Devil," Jagger-Richards, from *Beggars Banquet*, Decca Records, 1968.

CHAPTER 2: LOVE BITES

1. I first heard the story of "Nanaue the Shark Man" by residents of Waipi'o Valley and filled the story out with details from the version at www.to-hawaii.com/legends/nanaue.

2. Traditional song "Ulili E" sung and recorded by Izrael Kamakawawiole, Mountain Apple Records.

CHAPTER 4: SEASON OF THE WITCH

1. Title reference to Donovan's "Season of the Witch" from the album *Sunshine Superman*, Columbia Records, 1966. But I have to say, it's Richard Thompson's version that electrifies me.

2. "The Name" is a story I heard Jay Leeming tell in a live workshop. This is my written version based on listening

to Jay's oral version. For more info on Jay Leeming's work, see www.jayleeming.com.

CHAPTER 5: THE RATTLE OF BONES

1. This quote about bone memory from Martin Shaw appears in an April 4, 2017 interview with Rob Hopkins at www. robhopkins.net.

2. "All I Really Want to Do," Bob Dylan, from *Another Side of Bob Dylan*, Columbia Records, 1964.

CHAPTER 6: GOD IS A LIAR

My first exposure to Medusa was the 1981 film "Clash of the Titans." Most of this version of her story was written off the top of my head, though I did pick up some new details of the story in an article that can be found at www.greekmythology.com/Myths/Creatures/Medusa.

CHAPTER 7: EMOTION IN MOTION

"The Water is Wide," Scottish folk song.

CHAPTER 9: THE WILDERNESS YEARS

"The Moon Man," Chukchi story. I first heard this story in a live telling by Martin Shaw at The Block Island Poetry Project, Block Island, RI, USA. My version is a recollection written down from listening to Martin and an album called *Away and Close to Home*, by Noa Baum.

CHAPTER 10: A TRICKSTER'S LOVE

1. *Inanna, Queen of Heaven and Earth: Her Stories and Hymns from Sumer,* by Diane Wolkstein and Samuel Kramer, Harper and Row, 1983.

CHAPTER 11: CHOSEN BY THE LION

1. Title is a reference to a poem by Linda Gregg in a book of the same name: *Chosen by the Lion,* Graywolf Press, 1994.

2. I'm not sure where I first learned the story of "Psyche and Eros." A lot of the details I just knew and the story poured out of my hands because I had so embodied it, but the first time I heard it told in its entirety was at the Great Mother Conference in Damariscotta, Maine told by Martin Shaw.

CHAPTER 12: THE WHITE DOVE

1. *Inanna, Queen of Heaven and Earth: Her Stories and Hymns from Sumer,* by Diane Wolkstein and Samuel Kramer, Harper and Row, 1983.

CHAPTER 13: RUIN MEDICINE

1. The story of Hi'ilawe was first told to me by residents of Waipi'o Valley. A famous waterfall is named for these ill-fated lovers.

CHAPTER 14: THE WATER OF LIFE

1. "The Oldest Boy" is a story I heard in a workshop with storyteller Jay Leeming. I also listened to his telling of it on *The Crane Bag Podcast,* again told by Leeming. My version is a rendering of what I heard. www.jayleeming.com. *The Crane Bag Podcast* can be found on Apple Podcasts and Spotify.

CHAPTER 16: THE CRACKED MIRROR

1. First contact with this story was in the book, *Pele Mā: Legends of Pele from Kaua'i,* Frederick B. Wichman, Bamboo Ridge Press, 2001.

CHAPTER 18: THE KILLING MOON

1. Title chapter is a reference to the song "The Killing Moon" on the album *Ocean Rain* by Echo and the Bunnymen, unabashed romantics and the soundtrack to my first great love. *Ocean Rain,* Will Sergeant, Ian McCulloch, Les Pattinson, Pete de Freitas, Kovora Records, 1984.

2. "The Wind from Ha'ena," was inspired by a story I first read in *Pele Mā: Legends of Pele from Kauai,* Frederick B. Wichman, Bamboo Ridge Press, 2001. This story is an episode in the great Hawaiian epic, and equivalent to Homer's *Odyssey,* in which two sister goddesses, Pele and Hi'iaka, have many adventures that range from Moku o Keawe to Kauai.

CHAPTER 19: AND I SAY IT'S ALRIGHT

1. Title chapter is a riff on the Beatles tune "Here Comes the Sun" from *Abbey Road*. George Harrison, composer. Apple Records, 1969.

2. "Pursuit of Dermot and Grainne," Irish story I heard Martin Shaw tell live at the Great Mother Conference in Damariscotta, Maine, 2019. I also referenced Shaw's written version at: www.greatmotherconference.org/the-pursuit-of-dermot-and-grainne.

3. "Astral Weeks," from *Astral Weeks*, Van Morrison, Warner Bros. Records, 1968.

AFTERWORD

1. *Inanna, Queen of Heaven and Earth: Her Stories and Hymns from Sumer,* by Diane Wolkstein and Samuel Kramer, Harper and Row, 1983

BIBLIOGRAPHY

Akana, Colette Leimomi & Gonzalez, Kiele, *Hānau Ka Ua: Hawaiian Rain Names*, Kamehameha Publishing, 2015.

Knife, Rita. *The Water of Life: A Jungian Journey through Hawaiian Myth*, University of Hawaii Press, 1989.

Morrell, Rima A., *The Hawaiian Oracle: Animal Spirit Guides from the Land of Light*, New World Library, 2006.

Pukui, Mary Kawena, *'Ōlelo No'eau*, Bishop Museum Press, 1983.

Shaw, Martin. *Wolferland*, Cista Mystic Press, 2020.

Varez, Dietrich, *Pele and Hi'iaka: A Tale of Two Sisters*, Petroglyph Press, 2011.

Wichman, Frederick B., *Pele Mā: Legends of Pele from Kaua'i*, Bamboo Ridge, 2001.

ACKNOWLEDGMENTS

When I began this book, I defined myself by the Hawaiian proverb "Huleilua i na nalu o Laoniupoko"—the waves of Launiupoko toss this way and that. It's a way of saying a person is unsure of herself.

At the conclusion of this book I can now say of myself, *Huli ke alo i ka paia*—turn the face to the wall, a proverb said of one who has nothing to fear. Think about it, to go to sleep with your face to the wall leaves your back exposed. Grounded in my 'unihipili, I know I am safe. Uhane activated, I am confident I can face anything.

It's humbling how much generosity I've received on my journey, especially when I consider how little I was able to give back in my years of depression and suffering. To all those who reached out when I was too numb to even ask, thank you. With your blessings, you have shown me how I can become a blessing, and I vow to do my best to pass that forward.

The first person I'd like to thank specifically is a remarkable warrior woman, my dear friend, Renate Schilling. The first time I saw her she was 30 feet above me in a tree with a chain-saw yelling down at me to get out of the way. Once she determined I was able to keep up with her a bit, she took me under her wing and we had many adventures together on Moku o Keawe, living together in Honaunau and Kealakekua, where we passed together through some powerful initiations in the azure waters of the bays, grounding in after on the black lava rocks. Renate was one of the first people able to penetrate my amnesia about who I was. She couldn't fathom how I was poor, obscure, and unsuccessful in every way the world valued. Through her, I began to see what a powerful creator I was.

Following a deep inner call, Renate left her home in Germany and created a new life for herself on the Big Island, and then New Mexico, where she died eight years after we met from ovarian cancer just as the winter snows were melting. She had always been afraid of dying in the cold. Although I miss her, I'm forever grateful she died as the ground was thawing and was carried to her next adventure on a proverb that guided our time together: I ke kai ki holo—swimming into the ocean of the sun.

Throughout this book, I've mentioned the importance of two men whose bodies of work have influenced mine, Martin Shaw and Ke'oni Hanalei, but it's more than that. What Martin and Ke'oni have both shown me is true dedication to kiakahi, purpose, modeling the work and commitment it takes to fulfill, and most of all how devotion to purpose is an act of service that can ripple out in ways we may never imagine, may never get credit for, or even ever realize. The most important thing is to follow it and make a contribution.

Thank you to Marc Paisin, steward of Paliuli Farm in Honaunau, for providing me with a job during COVID that became much more than that. We met on the lava at "Two Step," the snorkel spot at Honaunau Bay, brought together by his sweet dog Onaona, and I ended up managing his Airbnbs and living with him on the farm on land that once provided the food for the ali'i who lived in the Pu'uhonua down below. My hope is that this book feeds the spirits of the modern sanctuary in the same way the land where it was written once provided the chiefs who lived there with physical sustenance.

While living at Paliuli, which, by the way translates as a Hawaiian version of the Garden of Eden, another incredible woman came into my life through Marc. Although I met Jada Delanay in the last weeks of her life, the time we shared transcended the limits of the clock. Living in the unspoken shadow of her rapidly approaching death, our souls touched. I've heard Martin Shaw say you don't really belong to a place until the bones of your ancestors are buried in the cemetery. Jada's bones, in the form of ashes, became part of this ceremony. You read in the book how I released a handful into the water, but I also planted some in the roots of a jacaranda at Paliuli. We both planted ourselves, one through death, one still living. We both go on.

Leigh Medeiros, who describes herself on her website as a screenwriter, author and story analyst, was the first reader of this book, providing me with a general overview of what was working in the book and what was missing when it was still a chaotic mess. Her ability to extract the book's potential helped me clarify and commit even more to the next 20 drafts! But more than that, Leigh's enthusiasm for my project and belief in the power of art to create change in a practical way, helped me believe I had something worthy to offer when I still didn't quite believe it. I don't know anyone more committed than Leigh to helping other artists while still producing her own work in multiple genres. Thank you Leigh!

Thanks to my brother Steven Lighty for the frontispiece image, a representation of Kamapua'a in three of his kino lau—pig, ama'u fern, and humuhumunuknukuapua'a, the hog-nosed triggerfish.

Providence Career and Technical Academy Graphic design student Ashley Mejia offered her talents to digitally render the piko symbol that is found throughout the book.

I knew I needed a really good, unsentimental and discriminating editor for the book because, well, I can be a little of both. To my delight, Norman Minnick, poet, publisher, editor, and educator, agreed to edit the book, and it is a much more coherent vessel because of his assistance. He is also the book designer who has presented you with what you'll hopefully regard as an object of beauty to hold in your hands, as well as a waterfall of words to cleanse your soul and replenish you for the work at hand as we merge currents in the river heading to the next world, all the while cherishing this one. I am beyond grateful for his elegant and meticulous eye and his patience with my technical floundering, but most of all for his belief in the book. This final result you are reading is our co-creation.

Finally, I'd like to thank my parents who summoned me into this human experience through their love for each other. To be created consciously by two people in love is no small blessing, and I am eternally grateful. Although I do not have children, this book is the result of our legacy.

A NOTE ON THE TYPE

The text is Alda, designed by native
Hawaiian typeface designer
Berton Hasebe (b. 1982).
Alda was developed
to be expressive
at very small
sizes.

Titles
are set in
Benton Sans,
a grotesque sans-
serif typeface designed by
Tobias Frere-Jones, based on
Morris Fuller Benton's News Gothic.

Milton Keynes UK
Ingram Content Group UK Ltd.
UKHW040331070923
428189UK00013B/175/J